Math **Diagnosis** and **Intervention** System

Booklet D

Measurement, Geometry,
Data Analysis, and Probability
in Grades K–3

Scott Foresman·Addison Wesley

enVisionMATH™

Overview of Math Diagnosis and Intervention System

The system can be used in a variety of situations:

- **During School** Use the system for intervention on prerequisite skills at the beginning of the year, the beginning of a topic, or the beginning of a lesson. Use for intervention during the Topic when more is needed beyond the resources already provide for the lesson.

- **After-school, Saturday school, summer-school (intersession) programs** Use the system for intervention offered in special programs.

The system provides resources for:

- **Assessment** Diagnostic Tests are provided. Each Diagnostic Test assesses the content for a grade. Use a test at the start of the year for entry-level assessment or anytime during the year as a summative evaluation.

- **Diagnosis** An item analysis identifies areas where intervention is needed.

- **Intervention** Booklets A–E in Part 1 and Booklets F–J in Part 2 identify specific concepts and assign a number to each concept, for example, A12 or E10. For each concept, there is a two-page Intervention Lesson that provides an instructional activity followed by practice. References for the Intervention Lessons are provided in teacher materials for *enVisionMATH*.

- **Monitoring** The Teacher's Guide provides both Individual Record Forms and Class Record Forms to monitor student progress.

Editorial Offices: Glenview, Illinois • Parsippany, New Jersey • New York, New York

Sales Offices: Boston, Massachusetts • Duluth, Georgia • Glenview, Illinois
Coppell, Texas • Sacramento, California • Mesa, Arizona

ISBN-13: 978-0-328-31119-4
ISBN-10: 0-328-31119-7

16 V069 12 11

Table of Contents

Table of Contents continued

Time

Name _____

Time

1.

2.

2   1   3

3.

1. Ask: *What is the boy doing in the first picture?* He is putting on his socks. *What are the people doing in the second picture?* They are watching a movie. *Which takes more time?* Watching a movie takes more time. Have children circle the activity that takes more time.
2. Have children look at the zoo pictures. Have children put a 1 under the picture that shows what happens first, a 2 under the picture that shows what happens next, and a 3 under the picture which shows what happens last.
3. Ask children what is happening in each picture and if it is morning, afternoon, or evening.

© Pearson Education, Inc.

Intervention Lesson D1   **91**

Name _____

Time (continued)

Circle the activity in each exercise that takes more time.

4.

5.

Write 1, 2, and 3, to order the events.

6.

3   1   2

© Pearson Education, Inc.

92   Intervention Lesson D1

Teacher Notes

Ongoing Assessment

Ask: *What is something you do in the morning? In the evening? In the afternoon?* Then ask which takes more time and name two of the events the child named.

Error Intervention

If children answer some of the exercises incorrectly,

then ask questions to talk them through the exercise. Ask them what is happening in each picture. Then ask questions like: *Does it take more time to eat a snack or to go shopping? Does the girl put on her life jacket before or after she gets into the canoe?*

If You Have More Time

Have children draw pictures to illustrate the order of three events, such as what they do to get ready for bed.

Days and Seasons

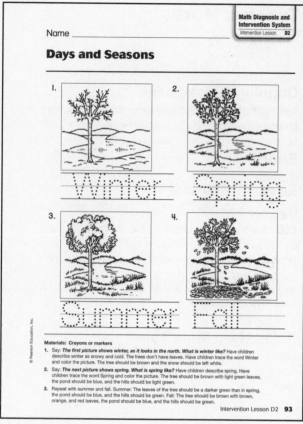

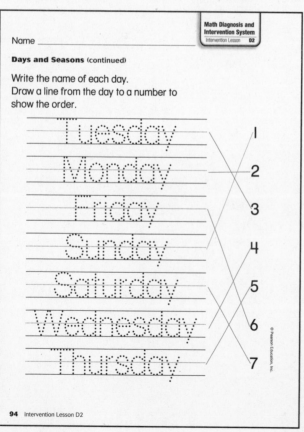

Teacher Notes

Ongoing Assessment

Ask children to say the days of the week in order, starting with Sunday. Let them use a calendar to help.

Error Intervention

If children live in a climate with mild seasonal changes,

then use photographs from magazines or the internet to illustrate seasonal differences farther north.

If You Have More Time

Have children choose a day of the week and draw a picture to show something they do that day.

Calendar

(Worksheet 1)

Name _____

Calendar

March

Sunday	Monday	(Tuesday)	Wednesday	Thursday	(Friday)	Saturday
				1	②	3
4	5	⑥	7	✗	⑨	10
✗	12	⑬	14	15	⑯	17
18	19	⑳	21	22	㉓	✗
25	26	㉗	✗	29	㉚	31

April

Sunday	Monday	Tuesday	Wednesday	Thursday	Friday	Saturday
1	2	③	4	5	⑥	7
8	✗	⑩	11	12	⑬	14

Materials: Crayons or markers
1. Have children trace and write the missing numbers on the calendars.
2. Have children circle Friday and all the dates in that column with red.
3. Have children circle Tuesday and all the dates in that column with blue.
4. Have children put an X through March 8, 11, 24, 28, and April 9.

Intervention Lesson D3   **95**

Teacher Notes

Ongoing Assessment
Tell children the date. Have them find it on a calendar and tell what day of the week it is.

Error Intervention
If children have trouble filling in the missing numbers,

then use A6: Numbers to 30 and A8: Counting to 100.

If You Have More Time
Have children create a calendar of the current month.

(Worksheet 2)

Name _____

Calendar (continued)

1. Write the numbers in the calendar.
2. Circle Thursday and all the dates in that column.
3. Circle Monday and all the dates in that column.
4. Put an X on December 6, 12, 22, and 30.

December

Sunday	(Monday)	Tuesday	Wednesday	(Thursday)	Friday	Saturday
		1	2	③	4	5
✗	⑦	8	9	⑩	11	✗
13	⑭	15	16	⑰	18	19
20	㉑	✗	23	㉔	25	26
27	㉘	29	✗	㉛		

Time to the Hour

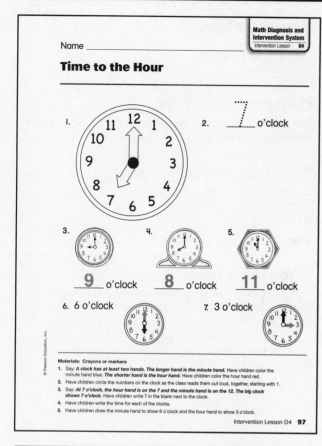

Name _____

Time to the Hour

1.

2. o'clock

3. **9** o'clock   4. **8** o'clock   5. **11** o'clock

6. 6 o'clock   7. 3 o'clock

Materials: Crayons or markers

1. Say: *A clock has at least two hands. The longer hand is the minute hand.* Have children color the minute hand blue. *The shorter hand is the hour hand.* Have children color the hour hand red.
2. Have children circle the numbers on the clock as the class reads them out loud, together, starting with 1.
3. Say: *At 7 o'clock, the hour hand is on the 7 and the minute hand is on the 12. The big clock shows 7 o'clock.* Have children write 7 in the blank next to the clock.
4. Have children write the time for each of the clocks.
5. Have children draw the minute hand to show 6 o'clock and the hour hand to show 3 o'clock.

Intervention Lesson D4   **97**

Teacher Notes

Ongoing Assessment
Ask: *Where are the hands on the clock at 2 o'clock?* The minute hand is on the 12 and the hour hand is on the 2.

Error Intervention
If children have trouble understanding the difference between the hour and minute hand,

then explain that the hour hand tells what hour it is. The hour hand takes one hour to move from one number to the next. The minute hand tells the minutes. The minute hand goes all the way around every hour and gets back to the 12 for each new hour.

If You Have More Time
Have children draw hands on clocks to show different times like 7 o'clock and 10 o'clock.

Name _____

Time to the Hour (continued)

Color the hour hand [red].
Circle the number to which it points.
Write the time.

8. _____ o'clock

9. **9** o'clock

10. **10** o'clock

11. **5** o'clock

12. **12** o'clock

13. **3** o'clock

98   Intervention Lesson D4

© Pearson Education, Inc.

---

4   Intervention Lesson D4

Time to the Half Hour

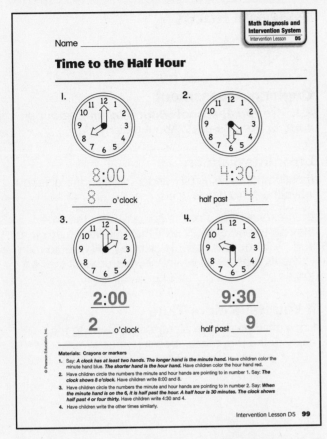

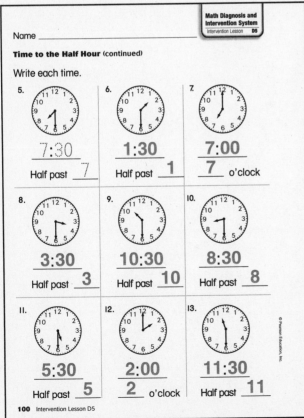

Teacher Notes

Ongoing Assessment

Ask: *Where is the hour hand on a clock at four thirty?* The hour hand is halfway between the 4 and the 5 because four thirty is halfway between 4 o'clock and 5 o'clock.

Error Intervention

If children have trouble telling time to the hour,

then use D4: Time to the Hour.

If You Have More Time

Write times to the hour and half hour on index cards. Give each pair of children about 6 cards and a student clock. One partner draws a card and shows the time on the clock. The other partner checks the answer. Then the second partner draws a card and shows the time while the first partner checks. Have them take turns until all the cards are used. You can draw picture of clocks on the index cards, showing each time, if necessary.

Ordering and Estimating Time

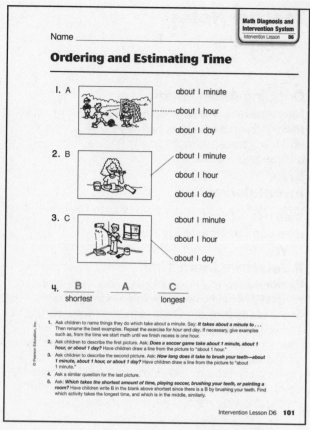

Name _____

Ordering and Estimating Time

1. A — about 1 minute / about 1 hour / about 1 day

2. B — about 1 minute / about 1 hour / about 1 day

3. C — about 1 minute / about 1 hour / about 1 day

4. B   A   C
   shortest   longest

1. Ask children to name things they do which take about a minute. Say: *It takes about a minute to . . .* Then rename the best examples. Repeat the exercise for *hour* and *day*. If necessary, give examples such as, from the time we start math until we finish recess is one hour.
2. Ask children to describe the first picture. Ask: *Does a soccer game take about 1 minute, about 1 hour, or about 1 day?* Have children draw a line from the picture to "about 1 hour."
3. Ask children to describe the second picture. Ask: *How long does it take to brush your teeth—about 1 minute, about 1 hour, or about 1 day?* Have children draw a line from the picture to "about 1 minute."
4. Ask a similar question for the last picture.
5. Ask: *Which takes the shortest amount of time, playing soccer, brushing your teeth, or painting a room?* Have children write B in the blank above shortest since there is a B by brushing your teeth. Find which activity takes the longest time, and which is in the middle, similarly.

Intervention Lesson D6   **101**

Teacher Notes

Ongoing Assessment
Ask: *Are you at school about a minute, about an hour, or about a day?* About a day

Error Intervention
If children have difficulty understanding the different ways the word day is used,

then explain that a day is actually from the time they go to bed at night until the next time they go to bed. Point out that people also say "all day" to refer to the time *between* when they get up until they go to bed.

If You Have More Time
Have children draw a picture of something they enjoy doing that takes about an hour.

Name _____

Ordering and Estimating Time (continued)

About how long does each activity take?
Draw lines to match.

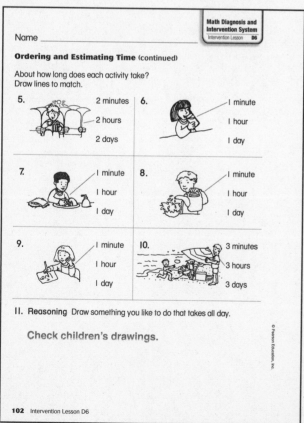

5. — 2 minutes / 2 hours / 2 days
6. — 1 minute / 1 hour / 1 day
7. — 1 minute / 1 hour / 1 day
8. — 1 minute / 1 hour / 1 day
9. — 1 minute / 1 hour / 1 day
10. — 3 minutes / 3 hours / 3 days

11. **Reasoning** Draw something you like to do that takes all day.

Check children's drawings.

Using a Calendar

Name _____

Using a Calendar

January	February	March

1. ‗12‗   2. ‗August‗

1. Say: *Each page in a calendar shows a month. This calendar shows a year. How many months are in a year?* Have children write 12.
2. Say the names of the months together as a class. Ask: *What month comes after July?* Have children write August. Say: *Find March 9th on the calendar. Circle it.*

Intervention Lesson D7   **103**

© Pearson Education, Inc.

Name _____

Using a Calendar (continued)

Use the calendar below.

April						
Sunday	Monday	Tuesday	Wednesday	Thursday	Friday	Saturday
			1	2	3	4
5	6	7	8	9	10	11
12	13	14	15	16	17	18
19	20	21	22	23	24	25
26	27	28	29	30		

Check student's coloring

3. Write the numbers in the calendar.

4. Color the first day of the month 🖍 RED .

5. Color all the Mondays 🖍 YELLOW .

6. Find the date one week after the 14th.
   Color that date 🖍 BLUE .

7. What is the date one week after April 15? **April 22**

© Pearson Education, Inc.

Teacher Notes

Ongoing Assessment

Have children look at the calendar in the activity and ask: *What date is one week after October 26?* November 2

Error Intervention

If children have trouble reading a calendar,

then use D3: Calendar.

If You Have More Time

Have children create a calendar for the month their birthday is in. Provide a blank calendar to help children find the day of the week their birthday month starts on. Have them say what day of the week their birthdays are.

Time to Five Minutes

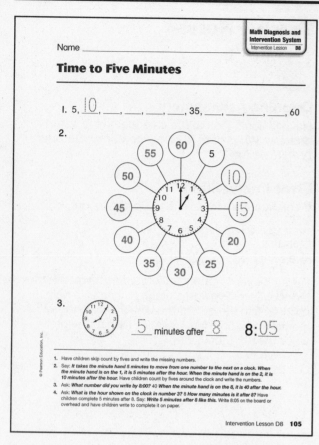

Name _____

Time to Five Minutes

Math Diagnosis and
Intervention System
Intervention Lesson   **D8**

1. 5, 10, ___, ___, ___, 35, ___, ___, ___, 60

2.

3.   5 minutes after 8   8:05

1. Have children skip count by fives and write the missing numbers.
2. Say: *It takes the minute hand 5 minutes to move from one number to the next on a clock. When the minute hand is on the 1, it is 5 minutes after the hour. When the minute hand is on the 2, it is 10 minutes after the hour.* Have children count by fives around the clock and write the numbers.
3. Ask: *What number did you write by 8:00?* 40 *When the minute hand is on the 8, it is 40 after the hour.*
4. Ask: *What is the hour shown on the clock in number 3?* 8 *How many minutes is it after 8?* Have children complete 5 minutes after 8. Say: *Write 5 minutes after 8 like this.* Write 8:05 on the board or overhead and have children write to complete it on paper.

Intervention Lesson D8   **105**

Teacher Notes

Ongoing Assessment
Ask: *Where is the minute hand at 20 minutes after 11?* On the 4

Error Intervention
If children confuse the hour and minute hands,

then use D4: Time to the Hour.

If You Have More Time
Have children work in pairs to create a game using index cards. Have them draw a clock showing 6:25 on one card, write 6:25 on another card, and write 25 minutes after 6 on a third card. Have children make at least ten sets of three cards with each set having a different time. Then, they can play "Time Rummy," drawing and discarding cards to try to match three card sets.

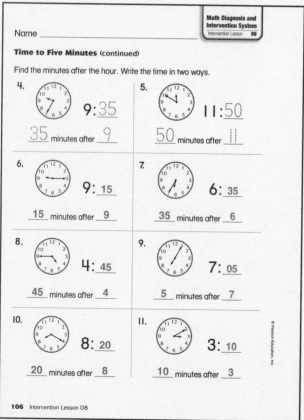

Name _____

Math Diagnosis and
Intervention System
Intervention Lesson   **D8**

Time to Five Minutes (continued)

Find the minutes after the hour. Write the time in two ways.

4.   9:35
     35 minutes after 9

5.   11:50
     50 minutes after 11

6.   9: 15
     15 minutes after 9

7.   6: 35
     35 minutes after 6

8.   4: 45
     45 minutes after 4

9.   7: 05
     5 minutes after 7

10. 8: 20
     20 minutes after 8

11. 3: 10
     10 minutes after 3

Time Before and After the Hour

Name _____

Time Before and After the Hour

1.

Before   After

2. 1 : **50**   **10** minutes before 2

3.   **30** minutes after 2

2 : **30**   half past 2

Materials: Crayons or Markers

1. Have children count by fives and fill in the circles up to 30. Then have them count by fives again and fill in the circles starting with 5 by the 11 on the clock, 10 by the 10, 15 by the 9 and so on. Explain that these numbers show how many minutes it is before the hour.
2. Ask: *What time is shown on the clock?* One fifty or fifty after one; Have children write 50. *When it is one fifty, how long is it until it is 2:00?* 10 minutes *Another way to say the time when it is one fifty or fifty after one is ten to two or ten minutes before two.* Have children trace 10.
3. Ask: *What time does the clock in item 3 show?* Have children write 30 twice. Say: *Another way to say two thirty or thirty after two is half past two.* Have children trace half past.

Intervention Lesson D9   **107**

Name _____

Time Before and After the Hour (continued)

Write the time more than one way.

4. 3 : **35**   **35** minutes after 3
                    25 minutes before 4

5. 3 : **45**   **45** minutes after 3
                    15 minutes before 4
                    quarter to 4

6. 8 : **30**   **30** minutes after 8
                    half past 8

7. 5 : **15**   **15** minutes after 5
                    quarter after 5

Reasoning Draw the hands on the clock to show the time.

8. It is quarter to 12.

9. It is half past 6.

Teacher Notes

Ongoing Assessment

Ask: *What is another way to say the time when it is seven forty-five?* Quarter to 8, 45 minutes after 7, or 15 minutes to 8

Error Intervention

If children have trouble writing times like 1:30 and 1:50,

then use D5: Time to the Half Hour and D8: Time to Five Minutes.

If You Have More Time

Have children draw a picture to show something they do at the same time every day. Have them draw a clock to show the time and then write the time before or after the hour.

Equivalent Times

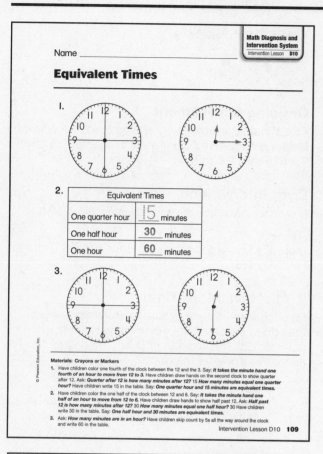

Materials: Crayons or Markers

1. Have children color one fourth of the clock between the 12 and the 3. Say: *It takes the minute hand one fourth of an hour to move from 12 to 3.* Have children draw hands on the second clock to show quarter after 12. Ask: *Quarter after 12 is how many minutes after 12?* 15 *How many minutes equal one quarter hour?* Have children write 15 in the table. Say: *One quarter hour and 15 minutes are equivalent times.*

2. Have children color the one half of the clock between 12 and 6. Say: *It takes the minute hand one half of an hour to move from 12 to 6.* Have children draw hands to show half past 12. Ask: *Half past 12 is how many minutes after 12?* 30 *How many minutes equal one half hour?* 30 Have children write 30 in the table. Say: *One half hour and 30 minutes are equivalent times.*

3. Ask: *How many minutes are in an hour?* Have children skip count by 5s all the way around the clock and write 60 in the table.

Intervention Lesson D10   **109**

Teacher Notes

Ongoing Assessment
Ask: *How many hours equal a day?* 24
How many minutes equal a half hour? 30

Error Intervention
If children have trouble shading a fourth or half of the clock,

then use A36: Understanding Fractions to Fourths and A38: Writing Fractions for Part of a Region.

If You Have More Time
Have children draw a picture of an activity they enjoy and write, in two different ways, how much time the activity takes.

Name _____

Equivalent Times (continued)

Use the schedule for Exercises 4 to 6.
Write 2 ways to say how long each event lasts.

4. Relay Race

   30 minutes

   one half hour

Field Day		
Event	Start	End
Parade	1:00	2:00
Relay Race	2:00	2:30
100 yd Dash	2:30	2:45

5. Parade   one hour   60 minutes

6. 100-Yard Dash   15 minutes   one quarter hour

Use the table for Exercises 7 to 8.

7. It has been 12 months since the last field day. What is another way to say 12 months?

   1 year

Equivalent Times	
1 day	24 hours
1 week	7 days
1 year	12 months

8. It took 1 week to plan field day. What is another way to say 1 week?   7 days

9. **Reasoning** How many days are equal to 2 weeks?   14 days

Comparing Temperatures

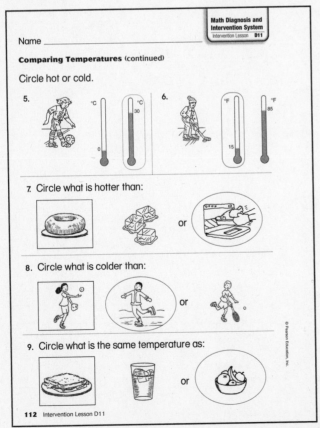

Teacher Notes

Ongoing Assessment

As a class, create a list of items that are hot to the touch and items that are cold to the touch. Discuss the items on the "hot" list and rank them in order from least hot to the most hot. Circle the items that are about the same temperature. Repeat with the items on the cold list.

Error Intervention

If children do not understand hot and cold,

then let them feel objects like warm bread or an ice cube. Identify each object as hot or cold and compare temperatures.

If You Have More Time

Discuss how the cement around an outdoor swimming pool in the summer time changes temperature throughout the day. Then discuss how the temperature of a glass of ice water changes if it is left outside on a hot day for a period of time.

Measuring Temperature

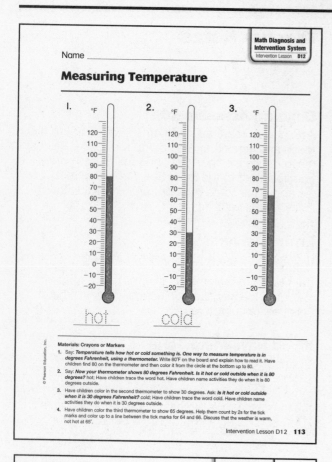

Name _____

Measuring Temperature

Materials: Crayons or Markers

1. Say: *Temperature tells how hot or cold something is. One way to measure temperature is in degrees Fahrenheit, using a thermometer.* Write 80°F on the board and explain how to read it. Have children find 80 on the thermometer and then color it from the circle at the bottom up to 80.

2. Say: *Now your thermometer shows 80 degrees Fahrenheit. Is it hot or cold outside when it is 80 degrees?* hot; Have children trace the word hot. Have children name activities they do when it is 80 degrees outside.

3. Have children color in the second thermometer to show 30 degrees. Ask: *Is it hot or cold outside when it is 30 degrees Fahrenheit?* cold; Have children trace the word cold. Have children name activities they do when it is 30 degrees outside.

4. Have children color the third thermometer to show 65 degrees. Help them count by 2s for the tick marks and color up to a line between the tick marks for 64 and 66. Discuss that the weather is warm, not hot at 65°.

Intervention Lesson D12   **113**

Teacher Notes

Ongoing Assessment

Ask: *Fifty-five degrees is between which two numbers on a thermometer?* 50 and 60

Error Intervention

If children do not understand how hot and cold relate to temperatures,

then use D11: Comparing Temperatures.

If You Have More Time

Have children color a thermometer to show the current outdoor temperature. Discuss if the temperature is considered hot, cold, or neither.

Name _____

Measuring Temperature (continued)

Write each temperature.
Then circle hot or cold.

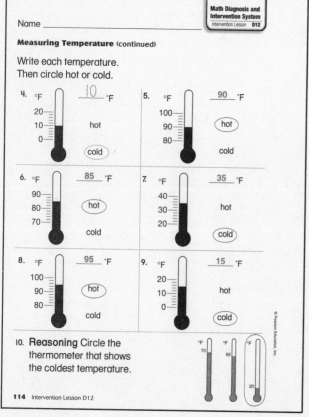

10. **Reasoning** Circle the thermometer that shows the coldest temperature.

114   Intervention Lesson D12

© Pearson Education, Inc.

Time to the Quarter Hour

Teacher Notes

Name _____

Time to the Quarter Hour

Use the clocks at the right to answer 1 to 6.

1. What two numbers is the hour hand between?

__12__ and __1__

2. Since the hour hand has not reached the 1, it is after 12:00. Write 12 for the hours in the digital clock.

3. What number is the minute hand on?   __3__

12:15
hours minutes

4. Each number on the clock represents 5 minutes after the hour. Count by 5s. How many minutes is it after 12?   __15__

5. Write 15 for the minutes in the digital clock.

The clock shows 12:15 or twelve fifteen.

6. Write 12:15 in two other ways.

15 minutes past __12__ ;   quarter past __12__

Use the clock at the right to answer 7 to 11.

7. What two numbers is the hour hand between?

__1__ and __2__

8. What is the hour? __1__

9. What number is the minute hand on?   __6__

10. Count by 5s. How many minutes is it after the hour?   __30__

11. Write the time in three ways.

__1__ : __30__ ; __30__ minutes past __1__ ; __half__ past __1__

Intervention Lesson D13 **115**

Name _____

Time to the Quarter Hour (continued)

For Exercises 12 to 15, use the clock at the right.

12. What time is shown on the clock?   __1__ : __45__

13. What hour is it about to be?   __2:00__

14. Count by 5s. How many minutes is it before 2 o'clock?   __15__

15. Write the time in two other ways.

15 minutes to __2__ ;   quarter to __2__

Write the hour and then the minutes after the hour. Then circle the two correct times.

16.
hour __2__
minutes __45__

(2:45)   3:45   1:45

quarter to 2   (15 minutes to 3)   quarter past 2

17.
hour __5__
minutes __15__

4:15   6:15   (5:15)

quarter past 6   (quarter past 5)   15 minutes to 5

18.
hour __8__
minutes __30__

7:30   (8:30)   9:30

(half past 8)   quarter past 8   30 minutes past 9

19.
11:45
hour __11__
minutes __45__

(11:45)   11:15   12:45

quarter to 11   15 minutes to 11   (quarter to 12)

© Pearson Education, Inc.

Ongoing Assessment

Ask: *What is another way to say 15 minutes past 4?* quarter past 4 or 4:15

Error Intervention

If students have trouble with time to the half hour,

then use D5: Time to the Half Hour.

If students have trouble finding how many minutes before or after an hour,

then use D8: Time to Five Minutes and D9: Time Before and After the Hour.

If You Have More Time

Put students in pairs. Have one student write the digital time to the whole, half, or quarter hours. Have the other student use the pupil's clock face to show the time. Remind the students that the hour hand is between two numbers when it is not an exact hour. Change roles and repeat.

Telling Time

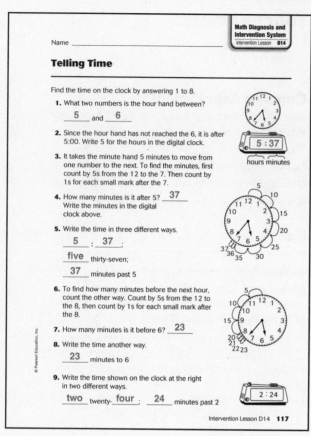

Name _____

Telling Time

Find the time on the clock by answering 1 to 8.

1. What two numbers is the hour hand between?

___5___ and ___6___

2. Since the hour hand has not reached the 6, it is after 5:00. Write 5 for the hours in the digital clock.

5 : 37
hours minutes

3. It takes the minute hand 5 minutes to move from one number to the next. To find the minutes, first count by 5s from the 12 to the 7. Then count by 1s for each small mark after the 7.

4. How many minutes is it after 5? ___37___
Write the minutes in the digital clock above.

5. Write the time in three different ways.

___5___ : ___37___ ;

___five___ thirty-seven;

___37___ minutes past 5

6. To find how many minutes before the next hour, count the other way. Count by 5s from the 12 to the 8, then count by 1s for each small mark after the 8.

7. How many minutes is it before 6? ___23___

8. Write the time another way.

___23___ minutes to 6

9. Write the time shown on the clock at the right in two different ways.

___two___ twenty- ___four___ ; ___24___ minutes past 2

2 : 24

Intervention Lesson D14   **117**

Teacher Notes

Ongoing Assessment

Ask: *Why do you count by 5s when you move from one number to the next on a clock?* It takes the minute hand 5 minutes to move from one number to the next, so there are 5 minutes between each number.

Error Intervention

If students have trouble differentiating the minute hand from the hour hand,

then use D4: Time to the Hour.

If students have trouble telling time to five minutes,

then use D8: Time to Five Minutes.

If You Have More Time

Write 3:16, 8:22, 10:37, and 11:52 on the board. Have students draw the analog clock face for each time. Remind students that the hour hand is between two numbers when it is not an exact hour.

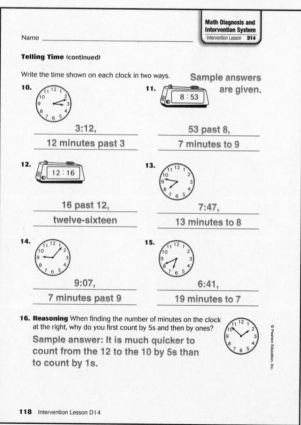

Name _____

Telling Time (continued)

Write the time shown on each clock in two ways.

Sample answers are given.

10.
___3:12,___
___12 minutes past 3___

11.
8 : 53
___53 past 8,___
___7 minutes to 9___

12.
12 : 16
___16 past 12,___
___twelve-sixteen___

13.
___7:47,___
___13 minutes to 8___

14.
___9:07,___
___7 minutes past 9___

15.
___6:41,___
___19 minutes to 7___

16. Reasoning When finding the number of minutes on the clock at the right, why do you first count by 5s and then by ones?

Sample answer: It is much quicker to count from the 12 to the 10 by 5s than to count by 1s.

118   Intervention Lesson D14

---

14   Intervention Lesson D14

© Pearson Education, Inc.

Units of Time

Math Diagnosis and
Intervention System
Intervention Lesson   **D15**

Name _____

Units of Time

Benny spent 3 weeks at his cousin's house. Find how many days
Benny spent at his cousin's by using the table and answering
1 to 3.

1. 1 week = __7__ days

Relating Units of Time		
1 week	=	7 days
1 day	=	24 hours
1 hour	=	60 minutes

2. To find how many days are in 3 weeks,
multiply 3 × 7 days.

3 × 7 days = __21__ days

3. How many days did Benny spend at his cousin's? __21__ days

The talent show lasted 2 hours and 17 minutes. Find how many
minutes the talent show lasted by using the table and answering
4 to 6.

4. 1 hour = __60__ minutes

5. First, find the number of minutes in 2 hours. Then add the
17 minutes.

2 × 60 minutes = __120__ minutes

120 minutes + 17 minutes = __137__ minutes

6. How many minutes did the talent show last? __137__ minutes

Cindy left her radio on for 4 days, 5 hours. Find how many hours
Cindy's radio stayed on by using the table and answering 7 to 9.

7. 1 day = __24__ hours

8. First find the number of hours in 4 days. Then add the 5 hours.

4 × 24 hours = __96__ hours

96 hours + 5 hours = __101__ hours

9. How many hours did Cindy's radio stay on? __101__ hours

Intervention Lesson D15   **119**

Teacher Notes

Ongoing Assessment

Ask: *Explain how you change 5 weeks, 3 days to
days.* First multiply 5 x 7 days to find the number of
days in 5 weeks. Then add the 3 days.

Error Intervention

If students cannot find the number of days in 3
weeks,

then have them color 3 weeks on a calendar.

If You Have More Time

Have students make up silly word problems that
involve time. For example: Mandy jumped and
sang Mary Had a Little Lamb for 2 hours and 13
minutes. How many minutes did Mandy jump and
sing? Have students trade problems with a partner
to solve.

Math Diagnosis and
Intervention System
Intervention Lesson   **D15**

Name _____

Units of Time (continued)

Find the missing numbers.

10. 6 hours = __360__ minutes   **11.** 8 days = __192__ hours

12. 9 weeks = __63__ days   **13.** 5 hours = __300__ minutes

14. 5 days, 3 hours = __123__ hours   **15.** 1 hour, 2 minutes = __62__ minutes

16. 6 weeks, 6 days = __48__ days   **17.** 3 days, 16 hours = __88__ hours

18. The first space flight when humans orbited the earth lasted
1 hour, 48 minutes.
How many minutes did the flight last?   108 minutes

19. The first space flight when humans orbited the moon
lasted 6 days, 3 hours. How many hours did the
mission last?   147 hours

20. It normally takes a duck egg 4 weeks, 2 days to
hatch. How many days is 4 weeks, 2 days?   30 days

21. It normally takes a pigeon egg 2 weeks, 4 days to
hatch. How many days is 2 weeks, 4 days?   18 days

22. **Reasoning** A chicken egg normally hatches in 21 days.
A turkey egg normally hatches in 3 weeks, 5 days. How
many more days does it normally take a turkey egg to
hatch than a chicken egg? Explain how you solved.

5 more days; 3 weeks is 3 × 7 = 21 days,
3 weeks 5 days is 21 + 5 = 26 days.
26 days – 21 days = 5 days.

23. Eddie ran a marathon in 4 hours and 7 minutes. His goal
was to finish the race in less than 250 minutes. Did Eddie
achieve his goal? Explain your reasoning.

Yes; 4 hours 7 minutes is 240 + 7 = 247
minutes. He finished the race 3 minutes faster
than his goal.

120   Intervention Lesson D15

Elapsed Time

Name _____

Math Diagnosis and
Intervention System
Intervention Lesson   **D16**

Elapsed Time

The party starts at 2:00 P.M. and ends at 4:45 P.M. How long is the party?

Start   **End**

1. How many hours from 2:00 P.M. to 4:00 P.M.?   __2__ hours
2. How many minutes from 4:00 P.M. to 4:45 P.M.?   __45__ minutes
3. How long did the party last?   __2__ hours, __45__ minutes

School starts at 8:20 A.M. and ends at 3:30 P.M. How long does school last?

Start   **End**

4. How many hours from 8:20 A.M. to 3:20 P.M.?   __7__ hours
5. How many minutes from 3:20 P.M. to 3:30 P.M.?   __10__ minutes
6. How long does school last?   __7__ hours, __10__ minutes

Reasoning The flight lasted 3 hours 20 minutes. If the plane took off at 4:10 P.M., what time did it land?

7. What time is 3 hours after 4:10 P.M.?   __7:10__ P.M.
8. What time is 20 minutes after 7:10 P.M.?   __7:30__ P.M.
9. What time did the plane land?   __7:30__ P.M.

Intervention Lesson D16   **121**

Name _____

Math Diagnosis and
Intervention System
Intervention Lesson   **D16**

Elapsed Time (continued)

Find the elapsed time.

10. Start Time: 1:00 P.M.
    End Time: 8:00 P.M.
    7 hours

11. Start Time: 7:00 A.M.
    End Time: 10:35 A.M.
    3 hours, 35 minutes

12. Start Time: 11:35 A.M.
    End Time: 3:50 P.M.
    4 hours, 15 minutes

13. Start Time: 6:10 P.M.
    End Time: 12:25 A.M.
    6 hours, 15 minutes

14. Start Time: 2:00 P.M.
    End Time: 6:05 P.M.
    4 hours, 5 minutes

15. Start Time: 9:20 A.M.
    End Time: 2:40 P.M.
    5 hours, 20 minutes

16. Start Time: 4:35 P.M.
    End Time: 5:15 P.M.
    40 minutes

17. Start Time: 8:15 A.M.
    End Time: 2:55 A.M.
    6 hours, 40 minutes

18. **Reasoning** The baseball game started at 3:00 P.M. It lasted 2 hours and 45 minutes. What time did the baseball game end?   **5:45 P.M.**

19. **Reasoning** Erin got home from the soccer match at 5:20 P.M. She went to bed 3 hours and 45 minutes later. What time did she go to bed?   **9:05 P.M.**

20. **Reasoning** The rainstorm began at 1:15 P.M. Marco's class came in from recess 25 minutes earlier. What time did the class come in from recess?   **12:50 P.M.**

21. **Reasoning** What is 30 minutes before 12:25 P.M.?   **11:55 A.M.**

122   Intervention Lesson D16

Teacher Notes

Ongoing Assessment

Ask: *Why do you not count hours first when finding the elapsed time from 8:40 A.M. to 9:10 A.M.?* Sample answer: If you counted hours you would go from 8:40 to 9:40, but the ending time is before 9:40, so you only count minutes.

Error Intervention

If students have trouble finding elapsed time mentally,

then encourage them to draw a clock face.

If You Have More Time

Print off flight schedules (that have minutes in multiples of 5) from an airport nearby showing departing and arrival times. Have students find the flight time (elapsed time) for each flight. Be sure to use flights in the same time zone.

Temperature

Name _____

Math Diagnosis and
Intervention System
Intervention Lesson   D17

Temperature

Temperature is the measure of how hot or how cold something is.

Temperature can be measured in **degrees Fahrenheit** (°F) or **degrees Celsius** (°C).

1. Look at the thermometer at the right. Does the right side show °F or °C?   °C

2. What is the temperature in °C?   20°C

Find the temperature in °F by answering 3 to 7.

3. Which side shows °F?   left

4. Look at the left side of the thermometer. How many spaces are between 30° and 40°?   5

5. What is 40° − 30°?   10°

6. Each space on the left side of the thermometer equals how many degrees? 10° ÷ 5 =   2°

7. Start at 60°F. Then count up by 2s to where the dark bar stops.

   60, 62, __64__, __66__, __68__

   The top of the dark bar is at 68, so the temperature is 68°F.

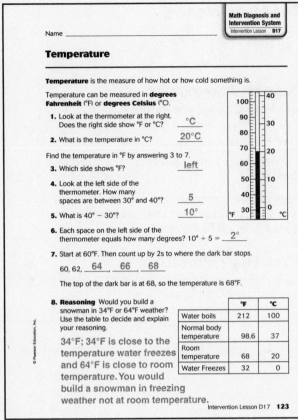

8. **Reasoning** Would you build a snowman in 34°F or 64°F weather? Use the table to decide and explain your reasoning.

   34°F; 34°F is close to the temperature water freezes and 64°F is close to room temperature. You would build a snowman in freezing weather not at room temperature.

	°F	°C
Water boils	212	100
Normal body temperature	98.6	37
Room temperature	68	20
Water Freezes	32	0

Intervention Lesson D17   **123**

© Pearson Education, Inc.

Teacher Notes

Ongoing Assessment

Ask: *Would you wear a coat outside if the temperature were 40°C? Why?* No, 40°C is very hot, swimming weather.

Error Intervention

If students have trouble reading a thermometer,

then use D12: Measuring Temperature.

If You Have More Time

Put students in pairs. Give the students a recent weather report for 6 places around the world, and a copy of a thermometer. Have partners mark and label each location's temperature. A map or globe may help students see how the weather is in different parts of the world.

Name _____

Math Diagnosis and
Intervention System
Intervention Lesson   D17

Temperature (continued)

Choose the better temperature for each activity.

9. bicycle riding   10. camping   11. ice skating   12. wearing shorts

   30°F or 70°F   0°C or 30°C   32°F or 72°F   35°C or 100°C

Choose the better estimate for the temperature.

13. hot pizza   14. ice cream   15. bathwater   16. cold drink

   80°F or 160°F   0°C or 30°C   45°F or 95°F   0°C or 10°C

Write each temperature in °F and °C.

17. __76__ °F   __24__ °C

18. __50__ °F   __10__ °C

19. __64__ °F   __18__ °C

20. __46__ °F   __8__ °C

21. __54__ °F   __12__ °C

22. __86__ °F   __30__ °C

23. One cold morning, the temperature was 35°F. The temperature rose to 53°F later in the day. How many degrees had the temperature increased?   18°F

24. **Reasoning** This morning the temperature was 65°F. Then it rose 3°. Then the temperature dropped 10°. What was the final temperature?   58°F

124   Intervention Lesson D17

© Pearson Education, Inc.

Comparing and Ordering by Length

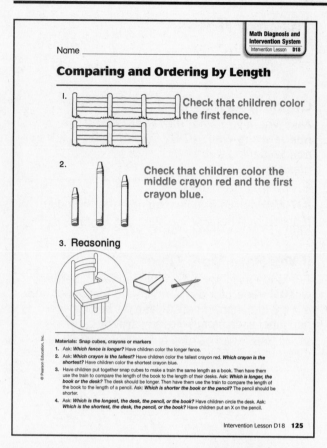

Name _____

Comparing and Ordering by Length

1. Check that children color the first fence.

2. Check that children color the middle crayon red and the first crayon blue.

3. Reasoning

Materials: Snap cubes, crayons or markers

1. Ask: *Which fence is longer?* Have children color the longer fence.
2. Ask: *Which crayon is the tallest?* Have children color the tallest crayon red. *Which crayon is the shortest?* Have children color the shortest crayon blue.
3. Have children put together snap cubes to make a train the same length as a book. Then have them use the train to compare the length of the book to the length of their desks. Ask: *Which is longer, the book or the desk?* The desk should be longer. Then have them use the train to compare the length of the book to the length of a pencil. Ask: *Which is shorter the book or the pencil?* The pencil should be shorter.
4. Ask: *Which is the longest, the desk, the pencil, or the book?* Have children circle the desk. Ask: *Which is the shortest, the desk, the pencil, or the book?* Have children put an X on the pencil.

Intervention Lesson D18   **125**

Teacher Notes

Ongoing Assessment
Ask: *Who is taller, you or me?*

Error Intervention
If children have trouble using the snap cubes to compare,

then let them compare directly. However, show them how they can use the cubes if they can't move the book to the desk.

If You Have More Time
Have children draw a picture of the people living in their homes from the shortest to the tallest.

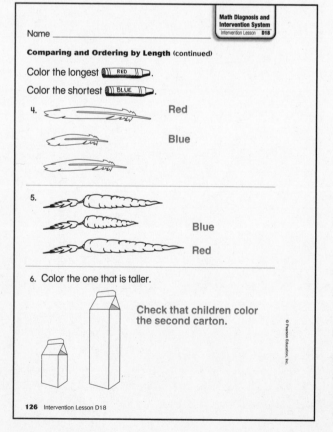

Name _____

Comparing and Ordering by Length (continued)

Color the longest 🖍 RED .
Color the shortest 🖍 BLUE .

4.   Red
       Blue

5.   Blue
       Red

6. Color the one that is taller.
   Check that children color the second carton.

126 Intervention Lesson D18

---

18 Intervention Lesson D18

Comparing and Ordering by Capacity

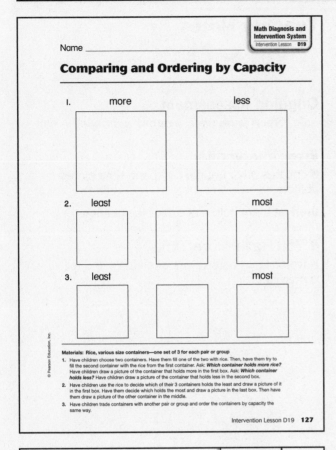

Name _____

Comparing and Ordering by Capacity

1. more   less

2. least   most

3. least   most

Materials: Rice, various size containers—one set of 3 for each pair or group

1. Have children choose two containers. Have them fill one of the two with rice. Then, have them try to fill the second container with the rice from the first container. Ask: **Which container holds more rice?** Have children draw a picture of the container that holds more in the first box. Ask: **Which container holds less?** Have children draw a picture of the container that holds less in the second box.

2. Have children use the rice to decide which of their 3 containers holds the least and draw a picture of it in the first box. Have them decide which holds the most and draw a picture in the last box. Then have them draw a picture of the other container in the middle.

3. Have children trade containers with another pair or group and order the containers by capacity the same way.

Intervention Lesson D19 **127**

© Pearson Education, Inc.

Teacher Notes

Ongoing Assessment

Ask: *You have a glass full of rice. You pour the rice into a cup until the cup is full. You still have rice left in the glass. Which holds more, the glass or the cup?* the glass

Error Intervention

If children have trouble comparing the pictured objects,

then let them look at real examples of each.

If You Have More Time

Have children name things that hold a lot of water, such as a swimming pool, a lake, and an ocean. Then have them decide which contains the most water.

Name _____

Comparing and Ordering by Capacity (continued)

Circle the one that holds more.

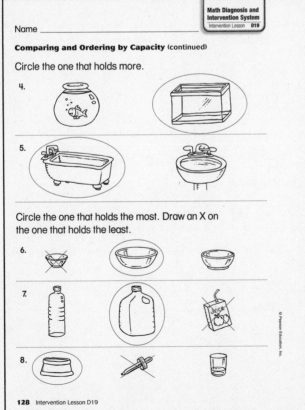

4.

5.

Circle the one that holds the most. Draw an X on the one that holds the least.

6.

7.

8.

128 Intervention Lesson D19

© Pearson Education, Inc.

Comparing and Ordering by Weight

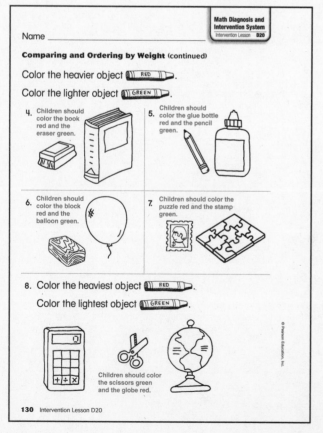

Comparing and Ordering by Weight

1.   heavier   lighter

2.   heaviest   lightest

3.   heaviest   lightest

Materials: Various objects of obviously different weights, one set of 3 for each pair or group.

1. Have children choose two of the objects. Have each child hold the objects, one in each hand to decide which is heavier and which is lighter. Have children draw a picture of the object which is heavier in the first box and the one which is lighter in the second box.
2. Have children decide which of their three objects is the heaviest and draw a picture in the first box. Have them decide which is the lightest and draw a picture in the last box. Have them draw a picture of the other object in the middle box.
3. Have children trade objects with another pair or group and order the objects by weight, the same way.

Intervention Lesson D20 **129**

Teacher Notes

Ongoing Assessment
Ask: *Which is heavier, a cat or a mouse?* A cat

Error Intervention
If children have trouble comparing the pictured objects,

then let them hold real examples of each.

If You Have More Time
Have children name pairs of animals and tell which is heavier.

Comparing and Ordering by Weight (continued)

Color the heavier object 🖍 RED 🖍.

Color the lighter object 🖍 GREEN 🖍.

4. Children should color the book red and the eraser green.

5. Children should color the glue bottle red and the pencil green.

6. Children should color the block red and the balloon green.

7. Children should color the puzzle red and the stamp green.

8. Color the heaviest object 🖍 RED 🖍.

Color the lightest object 🖍 GREEN 🖍.

Children should color the scissors green and the globe red.

Comparing Areas

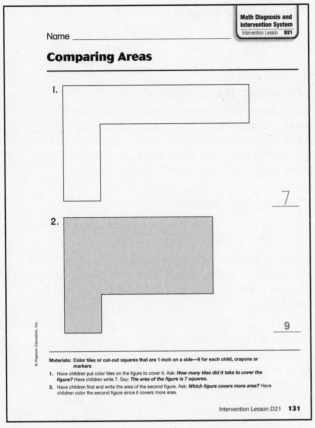

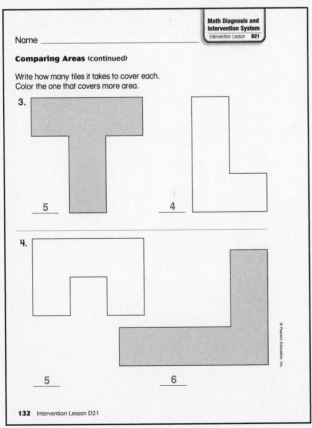

Teacher Notes

Ongoing Assessment

Have children brainstorm a list of places that cover more area than the classroom floor, such as the gym and cafeteria.

Error Intervention

If children have trouble counting the squares,

then use A1: Zero to Five and A3: Six to Ten.

If You Have More Time

Have children color as many 8 square unit shapes on a 10 by 10 grid as they can. Have children compare their findings with a partner.

Unit Size and Measuring

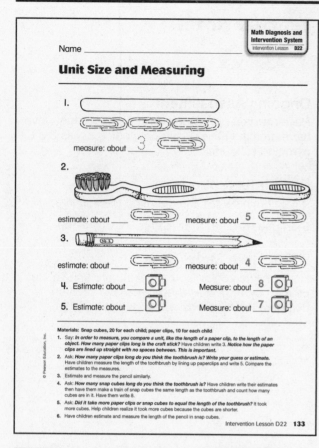

Teacher Notes

Ongoing Assessment

To determine if children understand that it takes more snap cubes than paper clips to equal a given length, see if their estimate of the length of the pencil in snap cubes is more than their measure of the length of the pencil in paper clips.

Error Intervention

If children do not line up the paper clips or snap cubes correctly,

then show them that the paper clips must start at one end of the object. Point out that there can be no gaps and the line of paper clips must be straight.

If You Have More Time

Let children combine their snap cubes to measure the length or height of items in the classroom, such as chairs, desks, and bookcases.

Inches and Feet

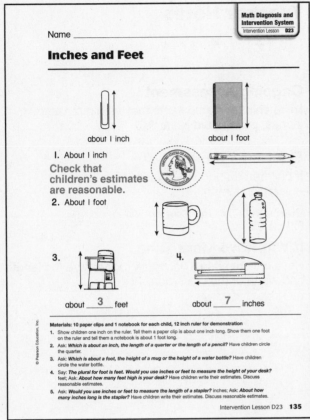

Name _____

Math Diagnosis and Intervention System
Intervention Lesson **D23**

Inches and Feet

about 1 inch   about 1 foot

1. About 1 inch
Check that children's estimates are reasonable.
2. About 1 foot

3. about ___3___ feet   4. about ___7___ inches

Materials: 10 paper clips and 1 notebook for each child, 12 inch ruler for demonstration
1. Show children one inch on the ruler. Tell them a paper clip is about one inch long. Show them one foot on the ruler and tell them a notebook is about 1 foot long.
2. Ask: *Which is about an inch, the length of a quarter or the length of a pencil?* Have children circle the quarter.
3. Ask: *Which is about a foot, the height of a mug or the height of a water bottle?* Have children circle the water bottle.
4. Say: *The plural for foot is feet. Would you use inches or feet to measure the height of your desk?* feet; Ask: *About how many feet high is your desk?* Have children write their estimates. Discuss reasonable estimates.
5. Ask: *Would you use inches or feet to measure the length of a stapler?* inches; Ask: *About how many inches long is the stapler?* Have children write their estimates. Discuss reasonable estimates.

© Pearson Education, Inc.

Intervention Lesson D23   **135**

Teacher Notes

Ongoing Assessment

Ask: **About how many feet tall do you think that I am?** Discuss which estimates make sense and which do not. Allow two children to measure your height and share the results with the class. Point out who had the best estimate.

Error Intervention

If children have trouble estimating,

then let them use paper clips and a notebook to measure real objects.

If You Have More Time

Have children name items they would measure in inches and items they would measure in feet.

Name _____

Math Diagnosis and Intervention System
Intervention Lesson **D23**

Inches and Feet (continued)

Circle the real objects that are about 1 inch.

5.

6.

Circle the objects that are about 1 foot.

7.

Reasoning Estimate.

8. about _____ inches   9. about _____ feet

Check that children's estimates are reasonable.

© Pearson Education, Inc.

136   Intervention Lesson D23

© Pearson Education, Inc.

Inches, Feet, and Yards

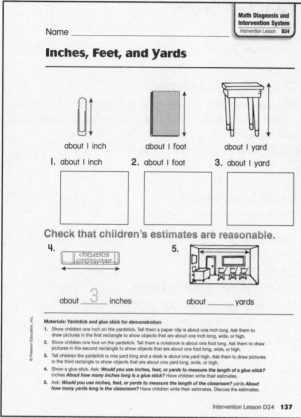

Name _____

Math Diagnosis and
Intervention System
Intervention Lesson D24

Inches, Feet, and Yards

about I inch   about I foot   about I yard

1. about I inch   2. about I foot   3. about I yard

Check that children's estimates are reasonable.

4.   5.

about __3__ inches   about _____ yards

Materials: Yardstick and glue stick for demonstration

1. Show children one inch on the yardstick. Tell them a paper clip is about one inch long. Ask them to draw pictures in the first rectangle to show objects that are about one inch long, wide, or high.

2. Show children one foot on the yardstick. Tell them a notebook is about one foot long. Ask them to draw pictures in the second rectangle to show objects that are about one foot long, wide, or high.

3. Tell children the yardstick is one yard long and a desk is about one yard high. Ask them to draw pictures in the third rectangle to show objects that are about one yard long, wide, or high.

4. Show a glue stick. Ask: **Would you use inches, feet, or yards to measure the length of a glue stick?** inches **About how many inches long is a glue stick?** Have children write their estimates.

5. Ask: **Would you use inches, feet, or yards to measure the length of the classroom?** yards **About how many yards long is the classroom?** Have children write their estimates. Discuss the estimates.

Intervention Lesson D24 **137**

Teacher Notes

Ongoing Assessment

Have children name items they would measure in inches, in feet, and in yards.

Error Intervention

If children do not understand the concept of measuring length,

then use D22: Unit Size and Measuring.

If You Have More Time

Have children use a yardstick to measure the length and width of the classroom.

Name _____

Math Diagnosis and
Intervention System
Intervention Lesson D24

Inches, Feet, and Yards (continued)

Estimate the width, height, or length of each real object.
Check that children's estimates are reasonable.

6.

length of a shoe

about _____ inches

7.

width of a window

about _____ feet

8.

height of a door

about _____ yards

9.

height of a classroom

about _____ yards

Circle the better estimate.

10.   A notebook is about 12 (inches) long.
                                yards

11.   A man is about 6 inches tall.
                          feet

138 Intervention Lesson D24

Inches

Name _____

Math Diagnosis and Intervention System
Intervention Lesson **D25**

Inches

Check that students' estimates are reasonable.

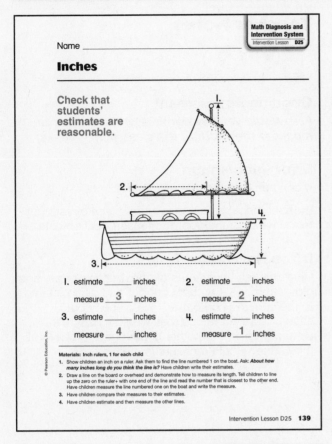

1. estimate _____ inches

   measure **3** inches

2. estimate _____ inches

   measure **2** inches

3. estimate _____ inches

   measure **4** inches

4. estimate _____ inches

   measure **1** inches

Materials: Inch rulers, 1 for each child

1. Show children an inch on a ruler. Ask them to find the line numbered 1 on the boat. Ask: *About how many inches long do you think the line is?* Have children write their estimates.
2. Draw a line on the board or overhead and demonstrate how to measure its length. Tell children to line up the zero on the ruler+ with one end of the line and read the number that is closest to the other end. Have children measure the line numbered one on the boat and write the measure.
3. Have children compare their measures to their estimates.
4. Have children estimate and then measure the other lines.

Intervention Lesson D25 **139**

Name _____

Math Diagnosis and Intervention System
Intervention Lesson **D25**

Inches (continued)

Use a ruler. Measure each dotted line on the house.
Color the lines to show how long each line is.

red = 1 inch   green = 3 inches
blue = 2 inches   yellow = 4 inches

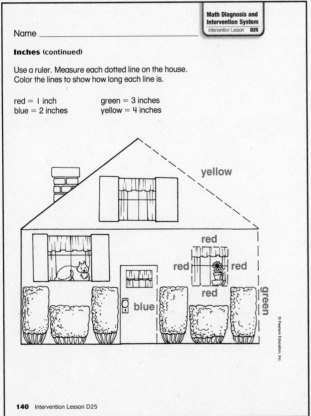

Teacher Notes

Ongoing Assessment

Make sure children can use and read a ruler correctly. Some common errors to watch for include not starting at the zero and not measuring in a straight line parallel to the object being measured.

Error Intervention

If children have trouble comparing a unit length to a given length,

then use D22: Unit Size and Measuring.

If You Have More Time

Have children estimate and then measure objects in the classroom to the nearest inch.

Centimeters and Meters

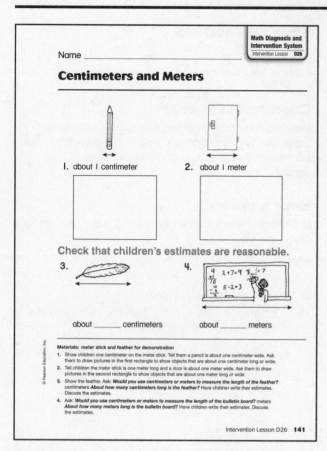

Centimeters and Meters

1. about 1 centimeter

2. about 1 meter

Check that children's estimates are reasonable.

3.

4.
9
2+7=9 3 □ = 7
+10
5-2=3
-4
3

about _____ centimeters

about _____ meters

Materials: meter stick and feather for demonstration

1. Show children one centimeter on the meter stick. Tell them a pencil is about one centimeter wide. Ask them to draw pictures in the first rectangle to show objects that are about one centimeter long or wide.

2. Tell children the meter stick is one meter long and a door is about one meter wide. Ask them to draw pictures in the second rectangle to show objects that are about one meter long or wide.

3. Show the feather. Ask: **Would you use centimeters or meters to measure the length of the feather?** centimeters **About how many centimeters long is the feather?** Have children write their estimates. Discuss the estimates.

4. Ask: **Would you use centimeters or meters to measure the length of the bulletin board?** meters **About how many meters long is the bulletin board?** Have children write their estimates. Discuss the estimates.

Intervention Lesson D26   **141**

Teacher Notes

Ongoing Assessment

Ask: *Would you use centimeters or meters to measure the width of the classroom?* meters

Error Intervention

If children have trouble estimating,

then let them use a pencil and a piece of yarn cut to the width of the door to measure real objects.

If You Have More Time

Give children two pieces of construction paper and old magazines. Let them cut out and glue pictures to the construction paper. One piece should have pictures of things they would measure in centimeters and the other should have pictures of things they would measure in meters.

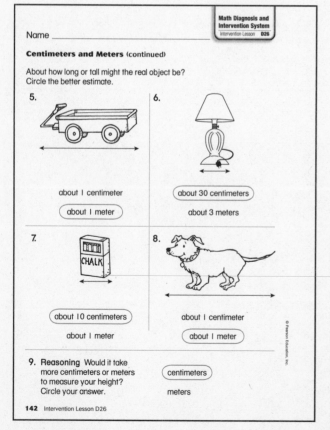

Centimeters and Meters (continued)

About how long or tall might the real object be?
Circle the better estimate.

5.

about 1 centimeter

about 1 meter

6.

about 30 centimeters

about 3 meters

7.

CHALK

about 10 centimeters

about 1 meter

8.

about 1 centimeter

about 1 meter

9. **Reasoning** Would it take more centimeters or meters to measure your height? Circle your answer.

centimeters

meters

142   Intervention Lesson D26

Centimeters

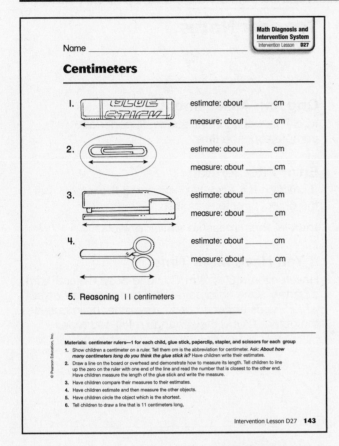

Teacher Notes

Ongoing Assessment

Make sure children line up and read rulers correctly. Some common errors to watch for include not starting at the zero and not measuring in a straight line parallel to the object being measured.

Error Intervention

If children confuse centimeters and inches,

then show both units on a ruler and explain they are actually very similar and can be used to measure the same things. Explain that inch is a customary unit and centimeter is a metric unit. The United States still uses customary units, but most of the rest of the world uses metric units.

If You Have More Time

Have children draw a rectangle with sides that are 5 centimeters and 9 centimeters.

Exploring Capacity

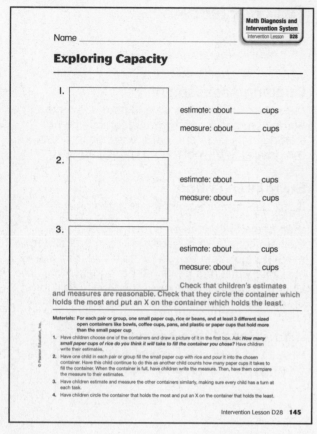

Name _____

Exploring Capacity

I. estimate: about _____ cups

measure: about _____ cups

2. estimate: about _____ cups

measure: about _____ cups

3. estimate: about _____ cups

measure: about _____ cups

Check that children's estimates
and measures are reasonable. Check that they circle the container which
holds the most and put an X on the container which holds the least.

Materials: For each pair or group, one small paper cup, rice or beans, and at least 3 different sized
open containers like bowls, coffee cups, pans, and plastic or paper cups that hold more
than the small paper cup

1. Have children choose one of the containers and draw a picture of it in the first box. Ask: **How many
small paper cups of rice do you think it will take to fill the container you chose?** Have children
write their estimates.

2. Have one child in each pair or group fill the small paper cup with rice and pour it into the chosen
container. Have this child continue to do this as another child counts how many paper cups it takes to
fill the container. When the container is full, have children write the measure. Then, have them compare
the measure to their estimates.

3. Have children estimate and measure the other containers similarly, making sure every child has a turn at
each task.

4. Have children circle the container that holds the most and put an X on the container that holds the least.

Intervention Lesson D28   **145**

Teacher Notes

Ongoing Assessment
Make sure children fill the small paper cup
completely each time.

Error Intervention
If children have trouble estimating the capacity of
the objects in the exercises,

then let them measure similar objects.

If You Have More Time
Have children play "I'm Thinking of an Object" with
a partner. One child says, *"I'm thinking of an object
which holds about 4 cups."* The other child guesses
the object. Then, they change roles and repeat.

Name _____

Exploring Capacity (continued)

Estimate how many cups each real object holds. Check that
children's estimates are reasonable.

4. estimate: about _____ cups

5. estimate: about _____ cups

6. estimate: about _____ cups

7. estimate: about _____ cups

8. **Reasoning** Circle the best estimate.

more than one cup   (less than one cup)

Cups, Pints, and Quarts

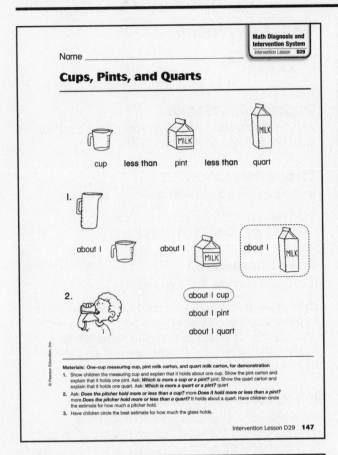

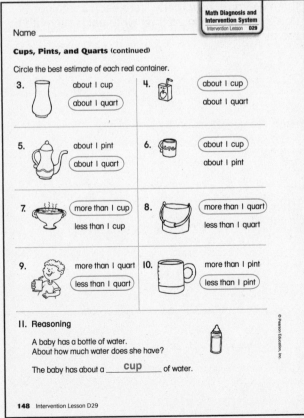

Teacher Notes

Ongoing Assessment

Ask: *Would you use a cup, a pint, or a quart to measure how much soup a large kettle can hold?* quart

Error Intervention

If children have trouble estimating capacities,

then use D19: Comparing and Ordering by Capacity and D28: Exploring Capacity.

If You Have More Time

Have children use a measuring cup, a pint container, and a quart container to measure the capacity of other containers.

Liters

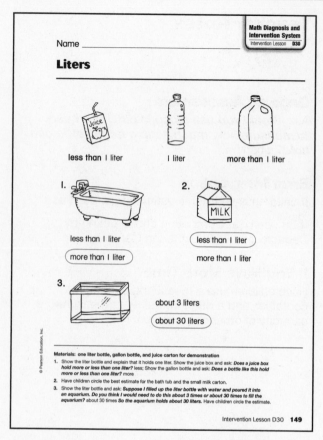

Name _____

Math Diagnosis and Intervention System

Intervention Lesson **D30**

Liters

less than I liter   I liter   more than I liter

I.

less than I liter

(more than I liter)

2.

(less than I liter)

more than I liter

3.

about 3 liters

(about 30 liters)

Materials: one liter bottle, gallon bottle, and juice carton for demonstration

1. Show the liter bottle and explain that it holds one liter. Show the juice box and ask: *Does a juice box hold more or less than one liter?* less; Show the gallon bottle and ask: *Does a bottle like this hold more or less than one liter?* more
2. Have children circle the best estimate for the bath tub and the small milk carton.
3. Show the liter bottle and ask: *Suppose I filled up the liter bottle with water and poured it into an aquarium. Do you think I would need to do this about 3 times or about 30 times to fill the aquarium?* about 30 times So the aquarium holds about 30 liters. Have children circle the estimate.

Intervention Lesson D30   **149**

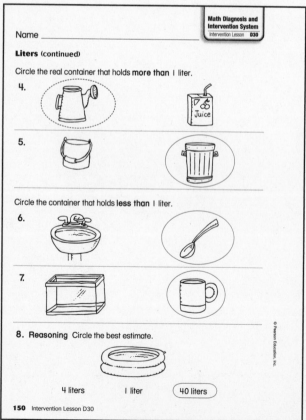

Name _____

Math Diagnosis and Intervention System

Intervention Lesson **D30**

Liters (continued)

Circle the real container that holds **more than** I liter.

4.

5.

Circle the container that holds **less than** I liter.

6.

7.

8. **Reasoning** Circle the best estimate.

4 liters   I liter   (40 liters)

Teacher Notes

Ongoing Assessment

Ask if something in your classroom, like a coffee cup, holds more or less than a liter.

Error Intervention

If children have trouble estimating capacities,

then use D19: Comparing and Ordering by Capacity and D28: Exploring Capacity.

Error Intervention

If children confuse liters and quarts,

then show a liter container and a quart container. Explain that the containers are actually very similar and can be used to measure the same things. Explain that quart is a customary unit and liter is a metric unit.

If You Have More Time

Give children constructions paper and old magazines. Let them cut out and glue pictures of 5 containers to the construction paper. Then, have them estimate how many liters each container holds. Children should then write each estimate by the picture.

Estimating and Measuring Weight

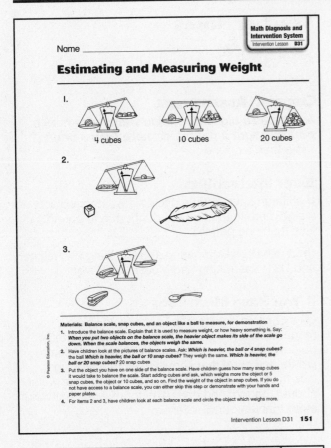

Teacher Notes

Ongoing Assessment
Ask: *How can you tell when two things weigh the same on a balance scale?* The scale balances when two things weigh the same.

Error Intervention
If children have trouble deciding which object is heavier,

then use D20: Comparing and Ordering by Weight.

If You Have More Time
Using a balance scale and snap cubes, let children take turns weighing different objects. Let the rest of the class watch and have them estimate the weight before each object is weighed.

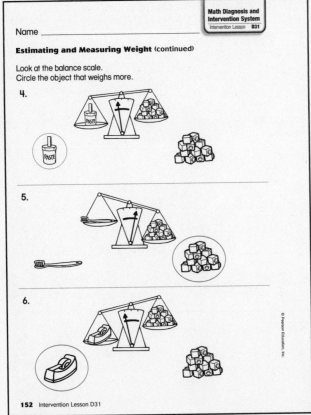

Pounds

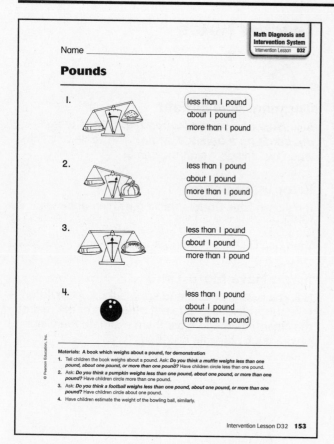

Name _____

Math Diagnosis and Intervention System
Intervention Lesson   D32

Pounds

1.
- less than 1 pound
- about 1 pound
- more than 1 pound

2.
- less than 1 pound
- about 1 pound
- more than 1 pound

3.
- less than 1 pound
- about 1 pound
- more than 1 pound

4.
- less than 1 pound
- about 1 pound
- more than 1 pound

Materials: A book which weighs about a pound, for demonstration

1. Tell children the book weighs about a pound. Ask: *Do you think a muffin weighs less than one pound, about one pound, or more than one pound?* Have children circle less than one pound.
2. Ask: *Do you think a pumpkin weighs less than one pound, about one pound, or more than one pound?* Have children circle more than one pound.
3. Ask: *Do you think a football weighs less than one pound, about one pound, or more than one pound?* Have children circle about one pound.
4. Have children estimate the weight of the bowling ball, similarly.

Intervention Lesson D32   **153**

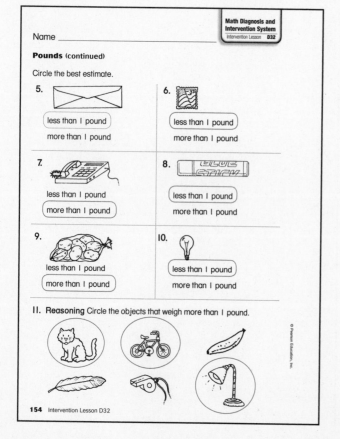

Name _____

Math Diagnosis and Intervention System
Intervention Lesson   D32

Pounds (continued)

Circle the best estimate.

5.
- less than 1 pound
- more than 1 pound

6.
- less than 1 pound
- more than 1 pound

7.
- less than 1 pound
- more than 1 pound

8.
- less than 1 pound
- more than 1 pound

9.
- less than 1 pound
- more than 1 pound

10.
- less than 1 pound
- more than 1 pound

11. **Reasoning** Circle the objects that weigh more than 1 pound.

Teacher Notes

Ongoing Assessment

Ask: *Does a big watermelon weigh less than a pound, about a pound, or more than a pound?* more than a pound

Error Intervention

If children have trouble deciding whether objects weigh more than one pound, about one pound, or less than one pound,

then use D20: Comparing and Ordering by Weight and D31: Estimating and Measuring Weight.

If You Have More Time

Give children construction paper and some magazines. Let them cut out and glue pictures of objects to the construction paper. Have children create one page that shows objects that weigh less than a pound, one page for objects that weigh about a pound, and one page for objects that weigh more than a pound.

Pounds and Ounces

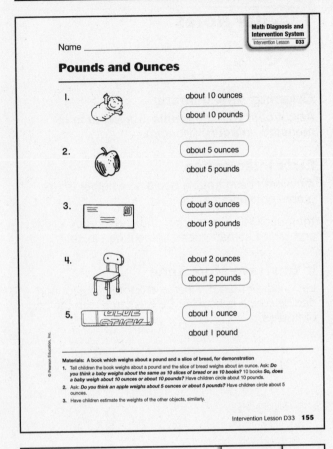

Name _____

Math Diagnosis and
Intervention System
Intervention Lesson   D33

Pounds and Ounces

1.   about 10 ounces
      about 10 pounds

2.   about 5 ounces
      about 5 pounds

3.   about 3 ounces
      about 3 pounds

4.   about 2 ounces
      about 2 pounds

5.   about 1 ounce
      about 1 pound

Materials: A book which weighs about a pound and a slice of bread, for demonstration
1. Tell children the book weighs about a pound and the slice of bread weighs about an ounce. Ask: *Do you think a baby weighs about the same as 10 slices of bread or as 10 books?* 10 books *So, does a baby weigh about 10 ounces or about 10 pounds?* Have children circle about 10 pounds.
2. Ask: *Do you think an apple weighs about 5 ounces or about 5 pounds?* Have children circle about 5 ounces.
3. Have children estimate the weights of the other objects, similarly.

Intervention Lesson D33   **155**

Name _____

Math Diagnosis and
Intervention System
Intervention Lesson   D33

Pounds and Ounces (continued)

Circle the best estimate.

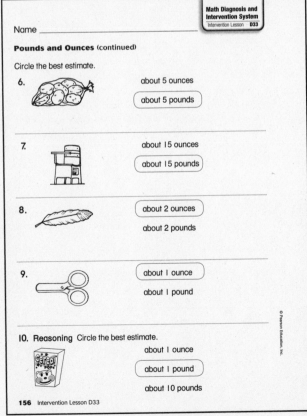

6.   about 5 ounces
      about 5 pounds

7.   about 15 ounces
      about 15 pounds

8.   about 2 ounces
      about 2 pounds

9.   about 1 ounce
      about 1 pound

10. **Reasoning** Circle the best estimate.
      about 1 ounce
      about 1 pound
      about 10 pounds

156 Intervention Lesson D33

Teacher Notes

Ongoing Assessment
Ask: *Would you measure the weight of a banana in ounces or pounds?* ounces

Error Intervention
If children have trouble estimating weights,

then use D20: Comparing and Ordering by Weight and D31: Estimating and Measuring Weight.

If You Have More Time
Have children name real life objects that they would weigh in ounces and objects they would weigh in pounds.

© Pearson Education, Inc.

Grams and Kilograms

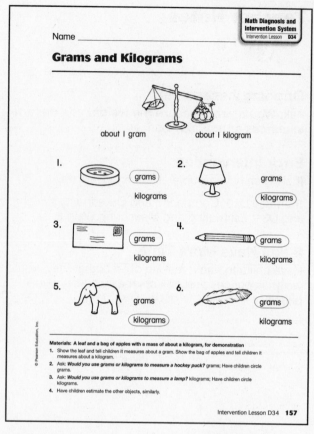

Name _____

Grams and Kilograms

about 1 gram   about 1 kilogram

1.   grams / kilograms

2.   grams / kilograms

3.   grams / kilograms

4.   grams / kilograms

5.   grams / kilograms

6.   grams / kilograms

Materials: A leaf and a bag of apples with a mass of about a kilogram, for demonstration

1. Show the leaf and tell children it measures about a gram. Show the bag of apples and tell children it measures about a kilogram.
2. Ask: *Would you use grams or kilograms to measure a hockey puck?* grams; Have children circle grams.
3. Ask: *Would you use grams or kilograms to measure a lamp?* kilograms; Have children circle kilograms.
4. Have children estimate the other objects, similarly.

Intervention Lesson D34   **157**

Teacher Notes

Ongoing Assessment

Ask: *Would you use grams or kilograms to measure an adult?* kilograms

Error Intervention

If children have trouble deciding whether to use grams or kilograms,

then use D20: Comparing and Ordering by Weight and D31: Estimating and Measuring Weight.

If You Have More Time

Let children hold the leaf and another object and decide which is heavier. Do the same with the bag of apples.

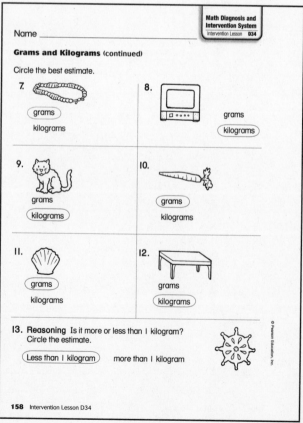

Name _____

Grams and Kilograms (continued)

Circle the best estimate.

7.   grams / kilograms

8.   grams / kilograms

9.   grams / kilograms

10.   grams / kilograms

11.   grams / kilograms

12.   grams / kilograms

13. **Reasoning** Is it more or less than 1 kilogram? Circle the estimate.

Less than 1 kilogram   more than 1 kilogram

Perimeter

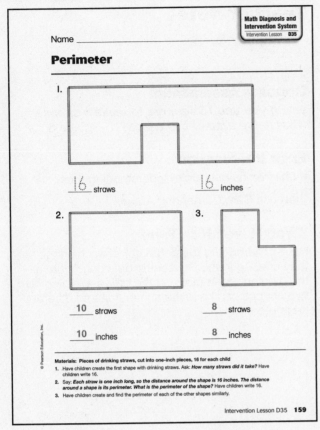

Name _____

Math Diagnosis and Intervention System

Intervention Lesson **D35**

Perimeter

1.

16 straws   16 inches

2.   3.

10 straws   8 straws

10 inches   8 inches

© Pearson Education, Inc.

Materials: Pieces of drinking straws, cut into one-inch pieces, 16 for each child

1. Have children create the first shape with drinking straws. Ask: *How many straws did it take?* Have children write 16.
2. Say: *Each straw is one inch long, so the distance around the shape is 16 inches. The distance around a shape is its perimeter. What is the perimeter of the shape?* Have children write 16.
3. Have children create and find the perimeter of each of the other shapes similarly.

Intervention Lesson D35 **159**

Name _____

Math Diagnosis and Intervention System

Intervention Lesson **D35**

Perimeter (continued)

Find the perimeter of each shape. Each straw is one inch long.

4.   5.

6 inches   8 inches

6.

14 inches

7. **Reasoning** Use 12 ▭━━━━▭.
Make a shape.
Draw it.
Check children's drawings.

© Pearson Education, Inc.

© Pearson Education, Inc.

Teacher Notes

Ongoing Assessment

Make sure children make a one-to-one correspondence between the pictured pieces of straw and the real pieces.

Error Intervention

If children do not know what an inch is,

then use D23: Inches and Feet.

If You Have More Time

In pairs, have children combine their pieces of straw. Pairs should then make as many different shapes as possible with 24 straws. Have them draw each shape.

Exploring Area

Name _____

Math Diagnosis and
Intervention System
Intervention Lesson   D36

Exploring Area

1. __6__ square units

2. __5__ square units
      Blue

3. __8__ square units   Red

Materials: Pattern blocks squares or cut-out squares that are $\frac{3}{4}$-inch on a side, up to 8 for each
child; crayons or markers

1. Ask: *How many squares does it take to cover the first shape?* Have children write 6.
2. Have children find the area of the other two shapes similarly.
3. Have children color the shape with the greatest area red. Ask: *How did you know that shape had the greatest area?* It has the greatest area because 8 is greater than 6 or 5.
4. Have children color the shape with the least area blue.

Intervention Lesson D36 **161**

Teacher Notes

Ongoing Assessment

Ask: *If you use 15 squares to make a shape, what is the area of the shape?* 15 square units

Error Intervention

If children have trouble understanding area,

then use D21: Comparing Areas.

If You Have More Time

Have children find the perimeter of each shape they created in the Reasoning question. Write all the different perimeters on the board. Discuss how two shapes can have the same area and different perimeters.

Name _____

Math Diagnosis and
Intervention System
Intervention Lesson   D36

Exploring Area (continued)

Find the area of each shape.

4.

area: __20__ square units

5.

area: __6__ square units

6.

area: __11__ square units

7.

area: __11__ square units

8. **Reasoning** Color two different shapes with an area of 10 square units. Use 2 colors.

Answers may vary.

© Pearson Education, Inc.

Measuring Length to $\frac{1}{2}$ and $\frac{1}{4}$ Inch

Name _____

Math Diagnosis and Intervention System
Intervention Lesson   D37

Measuring Length to $\frac{1}{2}$ and $\frac{1}{4}$ Inch

Materials inch ruler for each student, crayons or markers.

The distance between 0 and 1 on the ruler is one inch. So is the space between 1 and 2, 2 and 3, and so on.

1. Line up the left edge of the clothespin with the 0 mark on the ruler. Is the clothespin's length closer to the 2 inch mark or the 3 inch mark?   **3 inch mark**

2. What is the clothespin's length to the nearest inch?   **3 inches**

3. How many spaces are between 0 and 1 on the ruler above?   **4**

4. So each space is what part of an inch?   **$\frac{1}{4}$**

5. Color the marks in the ruler above that are $\frac{1}{4}$ inch and $\frac{3}{4}$ inch from zero red. Then color the rest of the $\frac{1}{4}$ inch marks red including $1\frac{1}{4}$, $1\frac{3}{4}$, $2\frac{1}{4}$, $2\frac{3}{4}$, and so on. Color the mark that is $\frac{2}{4}$ or $\frac{1}{2}$ inch from zero blue. Then color the rest of the $\frac{1}{2}$ inch marks blue, including $1\frac{1}{2}$, $2\frac{1}{2}$, and so on.

6. What is the length of the clothespin to the nearest $\frac{1}{2}$ inch?   **$2\frac{1}{2}$ inches**

Measure the length of the cricket to the nearest inch, $\frac{1}{2}$ inch and $\frac{1}{4}$ inch.

7. nearest inch   **1**   inch

8. nearest $\frac{1}{2}$ inch   **$1\frac{1}{2}$**   inches

9. nearest $\frac{1}{4}$ inch   **$1\frac{1}{4}$**   inches

© Pearson Education, Inc.

Intervention Lesson D37   **163**

Name _____

Math Diagnosis and Intervention System
Intervention Lesson   D37

Measuring Length to $\frac{1}{2}$ and $\frac{1}{4}$ Inch (continued)

Measure each object to the nearest inch, $\frac{1}{2}$ inch, and $\frac{1}{4}$ inch.

10. Nearest inch: **3** inches

11. Nearest $\frac{1}{2}$ inch: **3** inches

Nearest $\frac{1}{4}$ inch: **$2\frac{3}{4}$** inches

12. Nearest inch: **3** inches

13. Nearest $\frac{1}{2}$ inch: **$2\frac{1}{2}$** inches

Nearest $\frac{1}{4}$ inch: **$2\frac{3}{4}$** inches

14. Nearest inch: **1** inch

15. Nearest $\frac{1}{2}$ inch: **$1\frac{1}{2}$** inches

Nearest $\frac{1}{4}$ inch: **$1\frac{1}{4}$** inches

16. **Reasoning** Which gives the closest measurement, measuring to the nearest inch, $\frac{1}{2}$ inch, or $\frac{1}{4}$ inch? Explain.

Sample answer: Measuring to the nearest $\frac{1}{4}$ inch gives the closest measurement because there are more $\frac{1}{4}$ marks than $\frac{1}{2}$ inch or inch marks.

© Pearson Education, Inc.

164 Intervention Lesson D37

Math Diagnosis and Intervention System
Intervention Lesson   **D37**

Teacher Notes

Ongoing Assessment
Ask: *How long is your finger to the nearest $\frac{1}{4}$ inch?* Answers will vary.

Error Intervention
If students have trouble measuring to the nearest inch,

then use D25: Inches.

If You Have More Time

Have students choose 5 different objects in the classroom. Have them measure each to the nearest inch, $\frac{1}{2}$ inch, and $\frac{1}{4}$ inch. If time allows, have students take turns reporting their findings for one of the items they measured.

Using Customary Units of Length

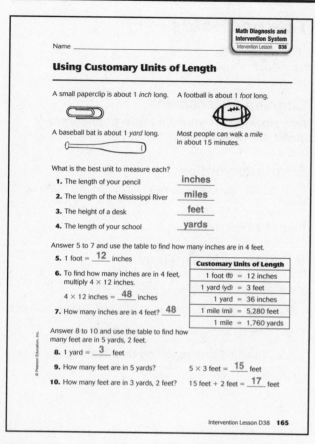

Name _____

Math Diagnosis and
Intervention System
Intervention Lesson   D38

Using Customary Units of Length

A small paperclip is about 1 *inch* long.   A football is about 1 *foot* long.

A baseball bat is about 1 *yard* long.   Most people can walk a *mile* in about 15 minutes.

What is the best unit to measure each?

1. The length of your pencil .... inches
2. The length of the Mississippi River ... miles
3. The height of a desk .... feet
4. The length of your school .... yards

Answer 5 to 7 and use the table to find how many inches are in 4 feet.

5. 1 foot = 12 inches

6. To find how many inches are in 4 feet, multiply 4 × 12 inches.

   4 × 12 inches = 48 inches

7. How many inches are in 4 feet? 48

Customary Units of Length	
1 foot (ft)	= 12 inches
1 yard (yd)	= 3 feet
1 yard	= 36 inches
1 mile (mi)	= 5,280 feet
1 mile	= 1,760 yards

Answer 8 to 10 and use the table to find how many feet are in 5 yards, 2 feet.

8. 1 yard = 3 feet

9. How many feet are in 5 yards?   5 × 3 feet = 15 feet

10. How many feet are in 3 yards, 2 feet?   15 feet + 2 feet = 17 feet

---

Name _____

Math Diagnosis and
Intervention System
Intervention Lesson   D38

Using Customary Units of Length (continued)

Which unit would you use to measure each item?
Write *inch*, *foot*, *yard*, or *mile*.

11. The length of a gerbil
    inch

12. The length of a football field
    yard

13. The height of a door
    foot

14. The distance to the sun
    mile

Circle the better estimate.

15. The distance you travel on an airplane

    560 yards   or   (560 miles)

16. The height of a full grown adult giraffe

    6 feet   or   (6 yards)

17. The length of a bar of soap

    (3 inches)   or   7 inches

18. The length of your bed

    (7 feet)   or   7 yards

Find each missing number.

19. 2 yards = 6 feet

20. 3 feet = 36 inches

21. 4 yards = 144 inches

22. 3 yards, 2 feet = 11 feet

23. 1 foot, 9 inches = 21 inches

24. 2 yards, 2 feet = 96 inches

25. **Reasoning** What unit would you use to measure the length of an earthworm? Explain why your choice is the best unit.

Inches; An earthworm is less than a foot long, so any unit other than inches would be too large.

Teacher Notes

Ongoing Assessment

Ask: *Why would you not measure the length of your school in inches?* Sample answer: My school is very long. It would be hard to give an accurate measurement in inches.

Error Intervention

If students have trouble visualizing an inch, foot, or yard,

then draw and label each length on the board. Students could also cut each length out of yarn.

If students have trouble visualizing a mile,

then give them an example of a building located about 1 mile from the school.

If students have trouble estimating inches, feet or yards,

then use D24: Inches, Feet, and Yards.

If You Have More Time

Cut 8 pieces of yarn the following lengths: 10 inches, 1 foot 2 inches, 1 foot 8 inches, 2 feet, 2 feet 3 inches, 2 feet 6 inches, 2 feet 9 inches, and 2 feet 11 inches. Put the yarn pieces in stations labeled A through H. Each student needs paper, pencil, and a ruler. Have groups of 3 rotate through the stations measuring the pieces of yarn in feet and inches and then converting the measurement to inches.

Using Metric Units of Length

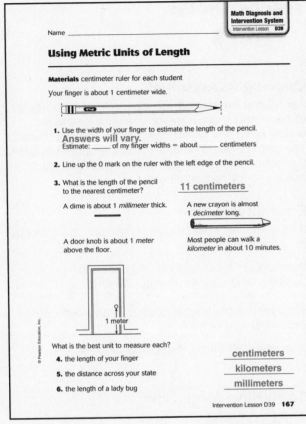

Name _____

Using Metric Units of Length

Materials centimeter ruler for each student

Your finger is about 1 centimeter wide.

1. Use the width of your finger to estimate the length of the pencil.
Answers will vary.
Estimate: _____ of my finger widths = about _____ centimeters

2. Line up the 0 mark on the ruler with the left edge of the pencil.

3. What is the length of the pencil
to the nearest centimeter?   **11 centimeters**

A dime is about 1 *millimeter* thick.   A new crayon is almost
1 *decimeter* long.

A door knob is about 1 *meter*   Most people can walk a
above the floor.   *kilometer* in about 10 minutes.

1 meter

What is the best unit to measure each?
4. the length of your finger   **centimeters**
5. the distance across your state   **kilometers**
6. the length of a lady bug   **millimeters**

© Pearson Education, Inc.

Intervention Lesson D39   **167**

Name _____

Using Metric Units of Length (continued)

Answer 7 to 9 and use the table to find how many centimeters
are in 4 meters, 76 centimeters.

7. 1 meter = __100__ centimeters

Metric Units of Length	
1 centimeter (cm)	= 10 millimeters
1 decimeter (dm)	= 10 centimeters
1 meter (m)	= 100 centimeters
1 kilometer (km)	= 1,000 meters

8. How many centimeters are
in 4 meters?

4 × 100 cm = __400__ cm

9. How many centimeters are in
4 meters, 76 centimeters?

400 cm + 76 cm = __476__ cm

Estimate the length of the spoon. Then measure to the
nearest centimeter.

10.

13 centimeters

What unit would you use to measure each item?
Write *millimeter, centimeter, decimeter, meter,* or *kilometer.*

11. An adult's height   **12.** Distance traveled on vacation
__meter__   __kilometer__

Choose the best estimate.

13. Length of a car   **14.** Length of a calculator
5 decimeters or (5 meters)   (12 centimeters) or 12 decimeters

Find each missing number.
15. 3 meters 18 centimeters = __318__ centimeters
16. 6 meters 3 centimeters = __603__ centimeters

© Pearson Education, Inc.

168   Intervention Lesson D39

Using Metric Units of Length

Teacher Notes

Ongoing Assessment
Ask: *Jane and Tela measured the distance
their turtles crawled. Jane wrote down 654
centimeters. Tela wrote down 8 meters and then
her pencil broke. Do you need to know what
else Tela was going to write to tell whose turtle
crawled farther?* No; Tela's turtle crawled farther
because 8 meters equals 800 centimeters and 800
is greater than 653. It doesn't matter how many
more centimeters Tela's turtle might have crawled.

Error Intervention
If students have trouble measuring to the nearest
centimeter,

then use D27: Centimeters.

If students have trouble estimating centimeters or
meters,

then use D26: Centimeters and Meters.

If You Have More Time
Have students draw an 8-sided irregular polygon on
their paper. Then trade with a partner and measure
each side to the nearest centimeter.

Using Customary Units of Capacity

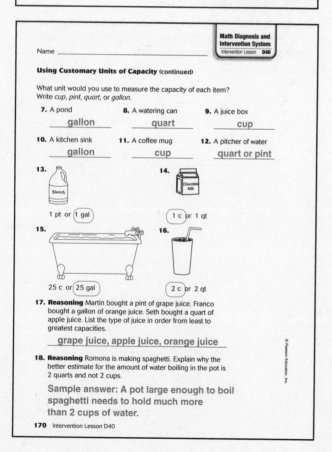

Name _____

Using Customary Units of Capacity

Materials 6 stations each equipped with the following: cup, pint, quart, and gallon measuring containers labeled with their units; one of 6 different sized containers to be measured labeled A, B, C, D, E, and F; enough rice to fill the container at least one and a half times; a piece of paper taped into a funnel for containers with small openings

The **capacity** of a container is the amount the container can hold.

Go to each station. Find the row in the table which matches the letter on the container. Complete the table by doing the following.

Customary Units of Capacity	
1 pint (pt)	= 2 cups (c)
1 quart (qt)	= 2 pints
1 gallon (gal)	= 4 quarts

• Decide what unit to use to measure the lettered container.

• Estimate the capacity of the container.

• Then measure the capacity of the container by filling the cup, pint, quart, or gallon container with rice and pouring it into the container until that container is full.

	Container	Best Unit	Estimate	Capacity
1.	A			
2.	B			
3.	C			
4.	D			
5.	E			
6.	F			

Answers will vary depending on containers.

Intervention Lesson D40 **169**

Name _____

Using Customary Units of Capacity (continued)

What unit would you use to measure the capacity of each item?
Write *cup, pint, quart,* or *gallon.*

7. A pond
gallon

8. A watering can
quart

9. A juice box
cup

10. A kitchen sink
gallon

11. A coffee mug
cup

12. A pitcher of water
quart or pint

13.
1 pt or (1 gal)

14.
1 c or 1 qt

15.
25 c or (25 gal)

16.
(2 c) or 2 qt

17. Reasoning Martin bought a pint of grape juice. Franco bought a gallon of orange juice. Seth bought a quart of apple juice. List the type of juice in order from least to greatest capacities.

grape juice, apple juice, orange juice

18. Reasoning Romona is making spaghetti. Explain why the better estimate for the amount of water boiling in the pot is 2 quarts and not 2 cups.

Sample answer: A pot large enough to boil spaghetti needs to hold much more than 2 cups of water.

170 Intervention Lesson D40

Teacher Notes

Ongoing Assessment
Ask: *If you measured the capacity of a container in cups and then in gallons, which measure would have the lesser number?* Sample answer: The gallons would have the lesser number because the gallon is much larger and it would take fewer gallons to fill the container.

Error Intervention
If students have trouble understanding the concept of capacity,

then use D19: Comparing and Ordering by Capacity and D28: Exploring Capacity.

If students have trouble distinguishing with cups, pints, and quarts,

then use D29: Cups, Pints, and Quarts.

If You Have More Time
Have students list other items that would be measured in cups, pints, quarts, and gallons.

© Pearson Education, Inc.

Using Metric Units of Capacity

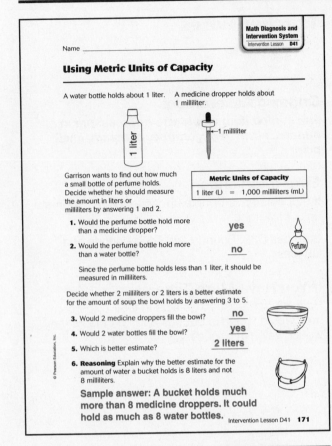

Name _____

Using Metric Units of Capacity

A water bottle holds about 1 liter. A medicine dropper holds about 1 milliliter.

1 liter

1 milliliter

Garrison wants to find out how much a small bottle of perfume holds. Decide whether he should measure the amount in liters or milliliters by answering 1 and 2.

Metric Units of Capacity	
1 liter (L)	= 1,000 milliliters (mL)

1. Would the perfume bottle hold more than a medicine dropper?   **yes**

2. Would the perfume bottle hold more than a water bottle?   **no**

Perfume

Since the perfume bottle holds less than 1 liter, it should be measured in milliliters.

Decide whether 2 milliliters or 2 liters is a better estimate for the amount of soup the bowl holds by answering 3 to 5.

3. Would 2 medicine droppers fill the bowl?   **no**

4. Would 2 water bottles fill the bowl?   **yes**

5. Which is better estimate?   **2 liters**

6. **Reasoning** Explain why the better estimate for the amount of water a bucket holds is 8 liters and not 8 milliliters.

Sample answer: A bucket holds much more than 8 medicine droppers. It could hold as much as 8 water bottles.

Intervention Lesson D41 **171**

© Pearson Education, Inc.

Name _____

Using Metric Units of Capacity (continued)

Choose a unit to measure the capacity of each item. Write *liters* or *milliliters*.

7. A can of soda
   milliliters

8. A swimming pool
   liters

9. A kitchen sink
   liters

10. A birdbath
   liters

11. A measuring spoon
   milliliters

12. A soup bowl
   milliliters

Circle the best estimate.

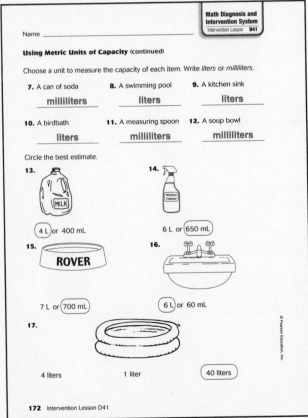

13.
MILK
(4 L) or 400 mL

14.
Window Cleaner
6 L or (650 mL)

15.
ROVER
7 L or (700 mL)

16.
(6 L) or 60 mL

17.
4 liters   1 liter   (40 liters)

© Pearson Education, Inc.

Teacher Notes

Ongoing Assessment

Ask: *If you measured the capacity of a container in milliliters and then in liters, which measure would have the greater number?* Sample answer: The number of milliliters would be greater because the milliliter is much smaller and it would take many more milliliters to fill the container.

Error Intervention

If students have trouble understanding the concept of capacity,

then use D19: Comparing and Ordering by Capacity and D28: Exploring Capacity.

If students have trouble estimating with liters,

then use D30: Liters.

If You Have More Time

Have students list other items that would be measured in milliliters and liters. Encourage them to be creative with their ideas for milliliters. For example, a screw top from a soda bottle that was left outside and filled with rainwater would be measured in millimeters.

Using Customary Units of Weight

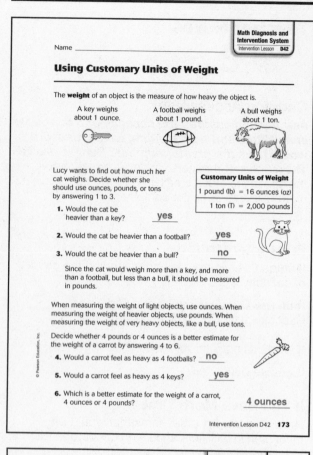

Math Diagnosis and Intervention System
Intervention Lesson D42

Name _____

Using Customary Units of Weight

The **weight** of an object is the measure of how heavy the object is.

A key weighs about 1 ounce.

A football weighs about 1 pound.

A bull weighs about 1 ton.

Lucy wants to find out how much her cat weighs. Decide whether she should use ounces, pounds, or tons by answering 1 to 3.

Customary Units of Weight

1 pound (lb) = 16 ounces (oz)

1 ton (T) = 2,000 pounds

1. Would the cat be heavier than a key? yes

2. Would the cat be heavier than a football? yes

3. Would the cat be heavier than a bull? no

Since the cat would weigh more than a key, and more than a football, but less than a bull, it should be measured in pounds.

When measuring the weight of light objects, use ounces. When measuring the weight of heavier objects, use pounds. When measuring the weight of very heavy objects, like a bull, use tons.

Decide whether 4 pounds or 4 ounces is a better estimate for the weight of a carrot by answering 4 to 6.

4. Would a carrot feel as heavy as 4 footballs? no

5. Would a carrot feel as heavy as 4 keys? yes

6. Which is a better estimate for the weight of a carrot, 4 ounces or 4 pounds? 4 ounces

Intervention Lesson D42 173

Teacher Notes

Ongoing Assessment

Ask: *Which item would you not measure in ounces: strawberry, orange, pumpkin, kiwi?* pumpkin

Error Intervention

If students have trouble understanding customary units of weight,

then use D32: Pounds and D33: Pounds and Ounces.

If You Have More Time

Have students list 10 objects in their classroom they would weigh in pounds and 10 objects they would weigh in ounces.

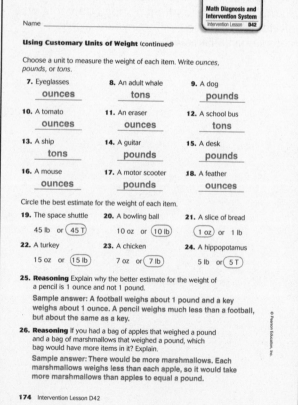

Math Diagnosis and Intervention System
Intervention Lesson D42

Name _____

Using Customary Units of Weight (continued)

Choose a unit to measure the weight of each item. Write *ounces, pounds,* or *tons.*

7. Eyeglasses ounces

8. An adult whale tons

9. A dog pounds

10. A tomato ounces

11. An eraser ounces

12. A school bus tons

13. A ship tons

14. A guitar pounds

15. A desk pounds

16. A mouse ounces

17. A motor scooter pounds

18. A feather ounces

Circle the best estimate for the weight of each item.

19. The space shuttle 45 lb or (45 T)

20. A bowling ball 10 oz or (10 lb)

21. A slice of bread (1 oz) or 1 lb

22. A turkey 15 oz or (15 lb)

23. A chicken 7 oz or (7 lb)

24. A hippopotamus 5 lb or (5 T)

25. **Reasoning** Explain why the better estimate for the weight of a pencil is 1 ounce and not 1 pound.

Sample answer: A football weighs about 1 pound and a key weighs about 1 ounce. A pencil weighs much less than a football, but about the same as a key.

26. **Reasoning** If you had a bag of apples that weighed a pound and a bag of marshmallows that weighed a pound, which bag would have more items in it? Explain.

Sample answer: There would be more marshmallows. Each marshmallows weighs less than each apple, so it would take more marshmallows than apples to equal a pound.

174 Intervention Lesson D42

Using Metric Units of Mass

Name _____

Math Diagnosis and
Intervention System
Intervention Lesson   D43

Using Metric Units of Mass

The amount of matter in an object is its **mass**.

A cantaloupe has
a mass of about
1 kilogram.

A grape has
a mass of about
1 gram.

1 gram

1 kilogram

Chi wants to find the mass of a bag of
potatoes. Decide whether he should
use grams or kilograms by answering
1 and 2.

Metric Units of Mass
1 kilogram (kg) = 1,000 grams (g)

1. Would the bag be heavier than
a grape?   yes

2. Would the bag be heavier than
a cantaloupe?   yes

Since the bag of potatoes has a mass greater than a grape, and
greater than a cantaloupe, it should be measured in kilograms.

When measuring the mass of lighter objects, use grams. When
measuring the mass of heavier objects, use kilograms.

Decide whether 300 kilograms or 300 grams is a better
estimate for the mass of a bag of pretzels by answering 3 to 5.

3. Would a bag of pretzels feel as heavy as
300 cantaloupes?   no

4. Would a bag of pretzels feel as heavy as
300 grapes?   yes

5. Which is the better estimate for the mass of
a bag of pretzels, 300 kilograms or 300 grams?   300 g

Intervention Lesson D43 **175**

Name _____

Math Diagnosis and
Intervention System
Intervention Lesson   D43

Using Metric Units of Mass (continued)

Choose a unit to measure the mass of each item. Write *grams*
or *kilograms*.

6. car kilograms   **7.** pencil grams

8. calculator grams   **9.** dog kilograms

10. key grams   **11.** hairbrush grams

12. flowerpot kilograms   **13.** flower grams

Choose the better estimate.

14.

Flour

200 g or (2 kg)

15.

(40 g) or 4 kg

16.

Crackers

(250 g) or 250 kg

17.

5 g or (5 kg)

18. Reasoning Why would you measure the mass of a goldfish
in grams and not kilograms?

Sample answer: A goldfish is lighter than a
cantaloupe, so kilograms is too large a unit.

19. Reasoning Explain why the better estimate for the mass of
a baby is 4 kilograms and not 4 grams.

Sample answer: A baby is much heavier than 4
grapes. It would feel more like 4 cantaloupes.

Teacher Notes

Ongoing Assessment

Ask: *Does a larger object always have a greater
mass than a smaller object? Explain why or why
not.* No; An empty box large enough for a television
is much larger than a brick, but the brick would
have a greater mass.

Error Intervention

If students have trouble understanding metric units
of mass,

then use D34: Grams and Kilograms.

If You Have More Time

Have students list 10 food items that would be
measured in kilograms and 10 food items that
would be measured in grams.

Perimeter

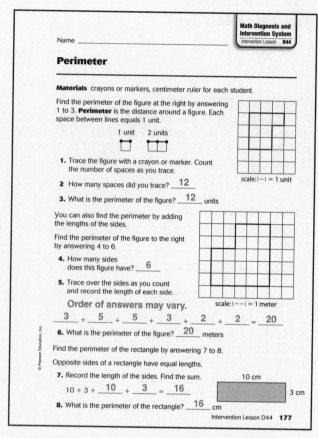

Name _____

Perimeter

Materials crayons or markers, centimeter ruler for each student.

Find the perimeter of the figure at the right by answering 1 to 3. **Perimeter** is the distance around a figure. Each space between lines equals 1 unit.

1 unit   2 units

1. Trace the figure with a crayon or marker. Count the number of spaces as you trace.

2 How many spaces did you trace? __12__

3. What is the perimeter of the figure? __12__ units

scale: |—| = 1 unit

You can also find the perimeter by adding the lengths of the sides.

Find the perimeter of the figure to the right by answering 4 to 6.

4. How many sides does this figure have? __6__

5. Trace over the sides as you count and record the length of each side.

Order of answers may vary.

__3__ + __5__ + __5__ + __3__ + __2__ + __2__ = __20__

scale: |—| = 1 meter

6. What is the perimeter of the figure? __20__ meters

Find the perimeter of the rectangle by answering 7 to 8.

Opposite sides of a rectangle have equal lengths.

7. Record the length of the sides. Find the sum.

10 + 3 + __10__ + __3__ = __16__

10 cm

3 cm

8. What is the perimeter of the rectangle? __16__ cm

Intervention Lesson D44 **177**

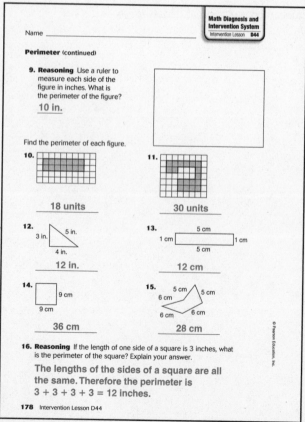

Name _____

Perimeter (continued)

9. Reasoning Use a ruler to measure each side of the figure in inches. What is the perimeter of the figure?

__10 in.__

Find the perimeter of each figure.

10. _____ 18 units

11. _____ 30 units

12. 3 in. 5 in. 4 in. _____ 12 in.

13. 5 cm 1 cm 1 cm 5 cm _____ 12 cm

14. 9 cm 9 cm _____ 36 cm

15. 5 cm 5 cm 6 cm 6 cm 6 cm _____ 28 cm

16. Reasoning If the length of one side of a square is 3 inches, what is the perimeter of the square? Explain your answer.

The lengths of the sides of a square are all the same. Therefore the perimeter is 3 + 3 + 3 + 3 = 12 inches.

Teacher Notes

Ongoing Assessment

Ask: *What are some real world examples that use the measure of the perimeter to solve a problem?* Sample answers: fencing, borders, picture frames, landscaping

Error Intervention

If students have trouble understanding the concept of perimeter,

then use D35: Perimeter.

If You Have More Time

Have students draw their names on a grid using block letters. They must only use vertical or horizontal lines, no diagonals. Have students find the perimeter of each letter in their names.

Finding Area on a Grid

Name _____

Finding Area on a Grid

Materials crayons or markers

Area is the number of square units needed to cover the region inside a figure.

Find the area of the rectangle by answering 1 and 2.

1. Color each grid square inside the rectangle. Count as you color. How many grid squares did you color? **12**

2. What is the area of the rectangle?
   12 square units

☐ = 1 square unit

Find the area of the polygon by answering 3 and 4.

3. Color each grid square inside the polygon. Count as you color. How many grid squares did you color? **24**

4. What is the area of the polygon? **24** square feet

☐ = 1 square foot

Estimate the area of the triangle by answering 5 to 8.

5. Color the whole squares blue. How many squares did you color? **6**

6. Combine partial square to make whole squares. Color the partial squares red. The partial squares make up about how many whole squares? **3**

7. Add. 6 + 3 = **9**

☐ = 1 square inch

8. What is the estimated area of the triangle?
   9 square inches

© Pearson Education, Inc.

Intervention Lesson D45   **179**

Name _____

Finding Area on a Grid (continued)

Find each area. Write your answer in square units.

9. **5 square units**

10. **9 square units**

11. **7 square units**

Find each area. Write your answer in square units.

12. **10 square units**

13. **10 square units**

14. **15 square units**

Judy baked several different shapes of crackers and wants to know which is largest. Each cracker was placed on a grid. Estimate the area of each cracker in Exercises 15 to 17.

15. Triangle **about 4 square units**

16. Hexagon **about 6 square units**

17. Quadrilateral **about 5 square units**

18. Which cracker in Exercises 15–17 has the greatest area?

   Exercise 16, the hexagon-shaped cracker

180   Intervention Lesson D45

© Pearson Education, Inc.

Teacher Notes

Ongoing Assessment

Ask: *How is the area of a rectangle different than the perimeter of a rectangle?* The area of a rectangle is the number of square units needed to cover the rectangle. The perimeter is the distance around the rectangle.

Error Intervention

If students have trouble understanding the concept of area,

then use D36: Exploring Area.

If You Have More Time

Give each pair of students an area in square units. Have the pairs of students draw as many rectangular figures on a grid as they can with that area. For example, if students are given an area of 10 square units, then the students could draw figures that are 1 unit by 10 units or 2 units by 5 units long. Have the students share their figures with the class. Encourage students to find the relationship between the sides of the rectangular figure and the area of the figure. ($A = L \times W$)

Counting Cubes to Find Volume

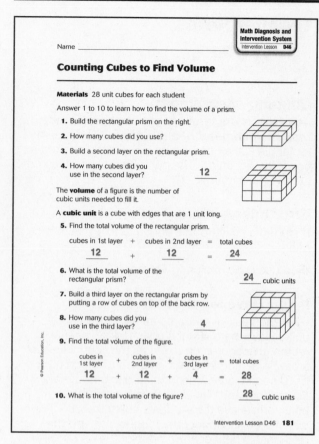

Name _____

Counting Cubes to Find Volume

Materials 28 unit cubes for each student

Answer 1 to 10 to learn how to find the volume of a prism.

1. Build the rectangular prism on the right.

2. How many cubes did you use?

3. Build a second layer on the rectangular prism.

4. How many cubes did you
   use in the second layer?   **12**

The **volume** of a figure is the number of
cubic units needed to fill it.

A **cubic unit** is a cube with edges that are 1 unit long.

5. Find the total volume of the rectangular prism.

   cubes in 1st layer + cubes in 2nd layer = total cubes
       12   +   **12**   =   **24**

6. What is the total volume of the
   rectangular prism?   **24** cubic units

7. Build a third layer on the rectangular prism by
   putting a row of cubes on top of the back row.

8. How many cubes did you
   use in the third layer?   **4**

9. Find the total volume of the figure.

   cubes in   cubes in   cubes in
   1st layer + 2nd layer + 3rd layer = total cubes
     12 + **12** + **4** = **28**

10. What is the total volume of the figure?   **28** cubic units

---

Name _____

Counting Cubes to Find Volume (continued)

Find the volume of each figure in cubic units.

11.   **18** cubic units

12.   **16** cubic units

13.   **18** cubic units

14.   **13** cubic units

15.   **26** cubic units

16.   **18** cubic units

17. **Reasoning** Yao made a rectangular prism with
    3 layers of cubes. He put 4 cubes in each layer.
    What is the volume of the rectangular prism?   **12** cubic units

18. **Reasoning** Box A consists of 8 cubic units. Three
    of Box A completely fills Box B. What is the volume
    of Box B?   **24 cubic units**

    A

    B

Teacher Notes

Ongoing Assessment

Ask: *Courtney used 16 cubes to make a
rectangular prism with 4 rows of 4 cubes
each. Explain why you do not have to do
any computations to find the volume of the
rectangular prism.* Sample answer: If Courtney
used 16 cubes then the volume will be 16 cubic
units.

Error Intervention

If students have trouble counting the hidden cubes,

then encourage them to use unit cubes to build
each solid.

If You Have More Time

Put students in pairs. Give each student 20 unit
cubes. Have one student in each pair build a solid
figure. Have the partner find the volume of the solid
without tearing the solid apart.

Position and Location

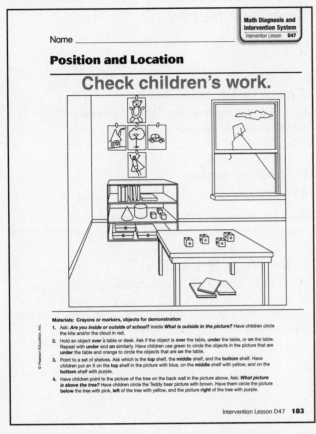

Name _____

Position and Location

Check children's work.

Materials: Crayons or markers, objects for demonstration

1. Ask: *Are you inside or outside of school?* inside *What is outside in the picture?* Have children circle the kite and/or the cloud in red.

2. Hold an object **over** a table or desk. Ask if the object is **over** the table, **under** the table, or **on** the table. Repeat with **under** and **on** similarly. Have children use green to circle the objects in the picture that are **under** the table and orange to circle the objects that are **on** the table.

3. Point to a set of shelves. Ask which is the **top** shelf, the **middle** shelf, and the **bottom** shelf. Have children put an X on the **top** shelf in the picture with blue, on the **middle** shelf with yellow, and on the **bottom** shelf with purple.

4. Have children point to the picture of the tree on the back wall in the picture above. Ask: *What picture is above the tree?* Have children circle the Teddy bear picture with brown. Have them circle the picture **below** the tree with pink, **left** of the tree with yellow, and the picture **right** of the tree with purple.

Intervention Lesson D47   **183**

Teacher Notes

Ongoing Assessment
Have children hold an object over, under, on, above, or below your outstretched hand.

Error Intervention
If children have trouble with left and right,

then have them hold up their left hand with their thumb perpendicular to the rest of their fingers. Tell them an L is formed and left starts with L.

If You Have More Time
Have children draw pictures showing different spacial relationships. Ask children to explain their picture to the class.

Name _____

Position and Location (continued)

Use the picture of the table below.

1. Draw ☐ above the table.

2. Draw △ **under** the table.

3. Draw ⬭ **right** of the hat.

Use the stack of bowls below.

4. Color the **bottom** [RED].

5. Color the **top** [ORANGE].

6. Color the **middle** [BLUE].

orange
blue
red

184 Intervention Lesson D47

Shapes

Name _____

Math Diagnosis and
Intervention System
Intervention Lesson   D48

Shapes

Check to see
that children
colored
correctly.

Materials: Crayons or Markers
1. Have children color all the circles green.
2. Have children color all the squares orange, and all the triangles blue.

Intervention Lesson D48   **185**

Teacher Notes

Ongoing Assessment
Ask: ***What shape is the face of the clock?*** circle
What shape is the door? rectangle

Error Intervention
If children have trouble telling the shapes apart,

then let them sort attribute blocks by shape and
name the circles, squares, rectangles, and triangles.

If You Have More Time
Have children create a picture using various
shapes. Children can then display their pictures in
class and share with the class the different shapes
they used to create the picture.

Name _____

Math Diagnosis and
Intervention System
Intervention Lesson   D48

Shapes (continued)

Color ☐ blue, △ green, ○ yellow.

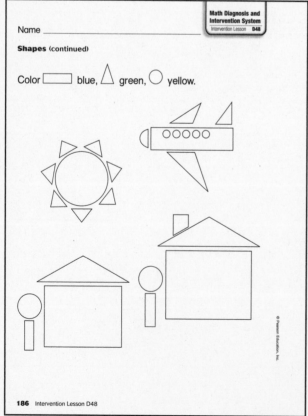

186 Intervention Lesson D48

Solid Figures

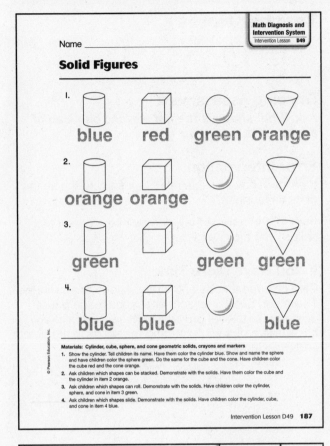

Name _____

Math Diagnosis and Intervention System
Intervention Lesson **D49**

Solid Figures

1.
blue   red   green   orange

2.
orange   orange

3.
green   green   green

4.
blue   blue   blue

Materials: Cylinder, cube, sphere, and cone geometric solids, crayons and markers

1. Show the cylinder. Tell children its name. Have them color the cylinder blue. Show and name the sphere and have children color the sphere green. Do the same for the cube and the cone. Have children color the cube red and the cone orange.
2. Ask children which shapes can be stacked. Demonstrate with the solids. Have them color the cube and the cylinder in item 2 orange.
3. Ask children which shapes can roll. Demonstrate with the solids. Have children color the cylinder, sphere, and cone in item 3 green.
4. Ask children which shapes slide. Demonstrate with the solids. Have children color the cylinder, cube, and cone in item 4 blue.

Intervention Lesson D49 **187**

Teacher Notes

Ongoing Assessment

Set out various geometric solids and ask each child to pick up the cylinder, cone, cube, or sphere.

Error Intervention

If children have trouble understanding how objects slide, roll, and stack,

then let them slide, roll, and stack the geometric solids.

If You Have More Time

Give children newspapers or magazines. Have children cut out pictures of objects shaped like each of the various types of solid and glue them to pieces of construction paper.

Name _____

Math Diagnosis and Intervention System
Intervention Lesson **D49**

Solid Figures (continued)

Circle the object with the same shape.

5.

6.

Circle the shape that slides.

7.   8.

Circle the shape that rolls.

9.   10.

Circle the shapes that stack.

11.   12.

Flat Surfaces of Solid Figures

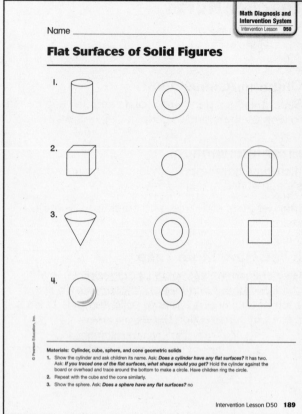

Name _____

Math Diagnosis and Intervention System
Intervention Lesson **D50**

Flat Surfaces of Solid Figures

1.

2.

3.

4.

Materials: Cylinder, cube, sphere, and cone geometric solids

1. Show the cylinder and ask children its name. Ask: *Does a cylinder have any flat surfaces?* It has two. Ask: *If you traced one of the flat surfaces, what shape would you get?* Hold the cylinder against the board or overhead and trace around the bottom to make a circle. Have children ring the circle.
2. Repeat with the cube and the cone similarly.
3. Show the sphere. Ask: *Does a sphere have any flat surfaces?* no

Intervention Lesson D50 **189**

Teacher Notes

Ongoing Assessment

Ask: *What shape is the flat surface on a can of soup?* circle

Error Intervention

If children have trouble relating a solid to the shape of its flat surface,

then let them trace the bottoms of the geometric solids onto a piece of paper.

If You Have More Time

Give children a cube and either a cone or a cylinder. These can be real objects or shapes made out of poster board. Also, provide paint so that children can make a picture by putting the solids in the paint and pressing them onto a piece of paper.

Name _____

Math Diagnosis and Intervention System
Intervention Lesson **D50**

Flat Surfaces of Solid Figures (continued)

Look at each shape.
Circle the object that has the flat surface.

5.

6.

7.

8.

9.

Properties of Plane Shapes

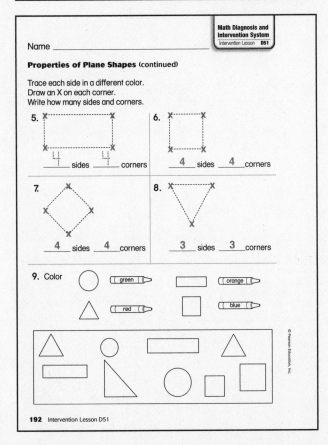

Teacher Notes

Ongoing Assessment

Ask: ***What does a corner feel like on the triangle?*** Possible Answer: The corner is sharp.

Error Intervention

If children count one side of a shape twice,

then have them color each side in their tracing as they count.

If You Have More Time

Have children work in pairs and play "Guess My Shape." Place the set of attribute blocks on the table between the two children. One partner describes a shape using words like, "It has 3 corners and 3 sides." The other partner chooses the attribute block that fits the description. Have children change roles and repeat until all the blocks have been chosen.

Making New Shapes from Shapes

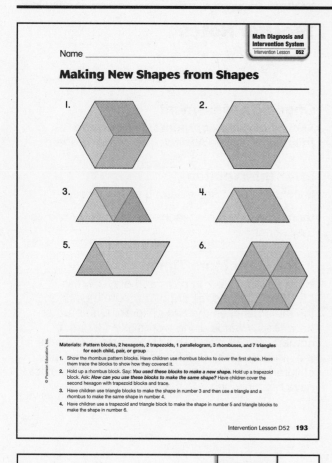

Making New Shapes from Shapes

1.
2.
3.
4.
5.
6.

Materials: Pattern blocks, 2 hexagons, 2 trapezoids, 1 parallelogram, 3 rhombuses, and 7 triangles
for each child, pair, or group

1. Show the rhombus pattern blocks. Have children use rhombus blocks to cover the first shape. Have them trace the blocks to show how they covered it.

2. Hold up a rhombus block. Say: *You used these blocks to make a new shape.* Hold up a trapezoid block. Ask: *How can you use these blocks to make the same shape?* Have children cover the second hexagon with trapezoid blocks and trace.

3. Have children use triangle blocks to make the shape in number 3 and then use a triangle and a rhombus to make the same shape in number 4.

4. Have children use a trapezoid and triangle block to make the shape in number 5 and triangle blocks to make the shape in number 6.

Intervention Lesson D52   **193**

Teacher Notes

Ongoing Assessment

Ask: *What do you get when you put two shapes together?* A new shape

Error Intervention

If children do not combine blocks correctly to make a larger shape,

then make sure they have enough pattern blocks to try to cover the larger shape. This way they can see the combination they had either does not fill the shape completely or more than fills it.

If You Have More Time

Let children draw a picture made out of shapes created by combining pattern blocks. Display the pictures in the classroom.

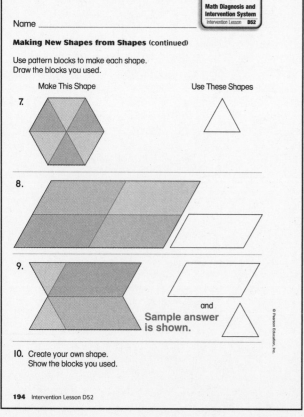

Making New Shapes from Shapes (continued)

Use pattern blocks to make each shape.
Draw the blocks you used.

Make This Shape   Use These Shapes

7.

8.

9.   and
Sample answer is shown.

10. Create your own shape.
Show the blocks you used.

194   Intervention Lesson D52

Cutting Shapes Apart

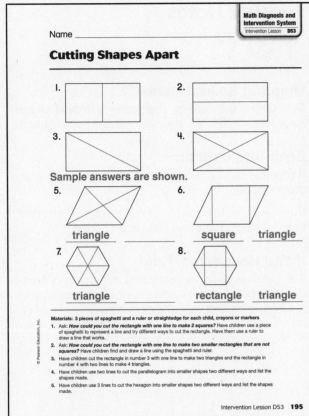

Cutting Shapes Apart

Name _____

Sample answers are shown.

5. triangle
6. square   triangle
7. triangle
8. rectangle   triangle

Materials: 3 pieces of spaghetti and a ruler or straightedge for each child, crayons or markers

1. Ask: **How could you cut the rectangle with one line to make 2 squares?** Have children use a piece of spaghetti to represent a line and try different ways to cut the rectangle. Have them use a ruler to draw a line that works.
2. Ask: **How could you cut the rectangle with one line to make two smaller rectangles that are not squares?** Have children find and draw a line using the spaghetti and ruler.
3. Have children cut the rectangle in number 3 with one line to make two triangles and the rectangle in number 4 with two lines to make 4 triangles.
4. Have children use two lines to cut the parallelogram into smaller shapes two different ways and list the shapes made.
5. Have children use 3 lines to cut the hexagon into smaller shapes two different ways and list the shapes made.

Intervention Lesson D53   **195**

Name _____

Cutting Shapes Apart (continued)

Draw lines to make new shapes. **Sample answers shown.**

9. Draw 1 line to make 2 triangles.

10. Draw 2 lines to make 4 squares.

11. Draw 3 lines to make 6 rectangles.

12. Draw 3 lines to make 6 triangles.

Draw the number of lines shown to make new shapes. Write the names of the shapes you made.

13. 1 line

triangle

14. 2 lines

rectangle   triangle

196   Intervention Lesson D53

Teacher Notes

Ongoing Assessment
Give children a sheet of paper and scissors. Ask them to cut the paper in one straight line to make 2 triangles.

Error Intervention
If children do not know the names of the basic shapes,

then use D48: Shapes or D51: Properties of Plane Shapes.

If You Have More Time
Photocopy the first page of the lesson onto construction paper. Let children cut out the larger shape. Then have them cut the shape into smaller shapes and name the smaller shapes.

© Pearson Education, Inc.

Same Size, Same Shape

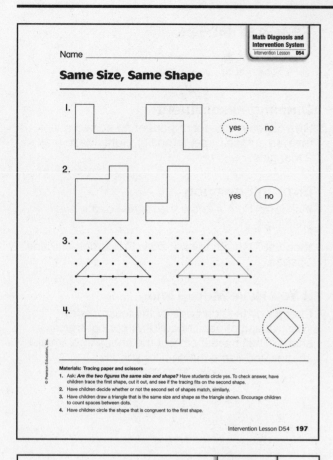

Same Size, Same Shape

I.   yes   no

2.   yes   no

3.

4.

Materials: Tracing paper and scissors

1. Ask: *Are the two figures the same size and shape?* Have students circle yes. To check answer, have children trace the first shape, cut it out, and see if the tracing fits on the second shape.
2. Have children decide whether or not the second set of shapes match, similarly.
3. Have children draw a triangle that is the same size and shape as the triangle shown. Encourage children to count spaces between dots.
4. Have children circle the shape that is congruent to the first shape.

Teacher Notes

Ongoing Assessment
Ask: *Can a triangle be the same size and shape as a rectangle?* No, they are not the same shape.

Error Intervention
If children have trouble drawing congruent shapes on dot paper,

then let them trace and cut out the first figure and use the tracing to draw the second figure.

If You Have More Time
Ask children to name real world examples of figures that are the same size and shape. Some examples are floor tiles and wall-paper patterns.

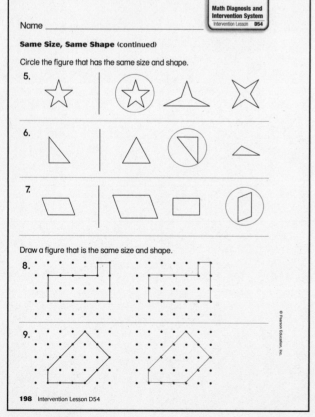

Same Size, Same Shape (continued)

Circle the figure that has the same size and shape.

5.

6.

7.

Draw a figure that is the same size and shape.

8.

9.

Ways to Move Shapes

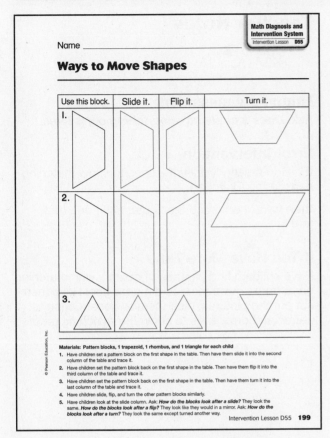

Name _____

Ways to Move Shapes

Use this block.	Slide it.	Flip it.	Turn it.
1.			
2.			
3.			

Materials: Pattern blocks, 1 trapezoid, 1 rhombus, and 1 triangle for each child

1. Have children set a pattern block on the first shape in the table. Then have them slide it into the second column of the table and trace it.
2. Have children set the pattern block back on the first shape in the table. Then have them flip it into the third column of the table and trace it.
3. Have children set the pattern block back on the first shape in the table. Then have them turn it into the last column of the table and trace it.
4. Have children slide, flip, and turn the other pattern blocks similarly.
5. Have children look at the slide column. Ask: *How do the blocks look after a slide?* They look the same. *How do the blocks look after a flip?* They look like they would in a mirror. Ask: *How do the blocks look after a turn?* They look the same except turned another way.

Intervention Lesson D55   **199**

Teacher Notes

Ongoing Assessment

Ask children to hold up their hands so the right hand is a slide, flip, or turn of the left.

Error Intervention

If children do not choose the motion used correctly,

then let them use pattern blocks. Have them set a block on the one shape and slide, flip, and turn the block until it looks like the other shape.

If You Have More Time

Have children name examples of slides, flips, and turns in the real world. Floor or wall tiles usually show a slide, reflections in a mirror and some designs show flips, and the hands of a clock shows a turn.

Name _____

Ways to Move Shapes (continued)

Is it a slide, flip, or turn?

4.   (slide)   flip   turn

5.   slide   (flip)   turn

6.   slide   flip   (turn)

7.   slide   (flip)   turn

8.   slide   flip   (turn)

9.   (slide)   flip   turn

Symmetry

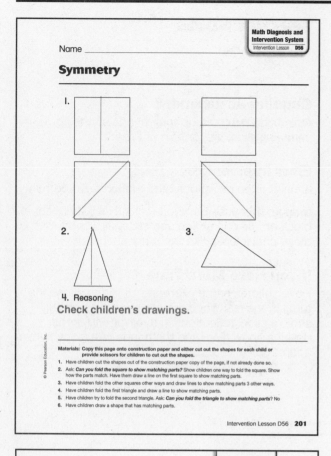

Materials: Copy this page onto construction paper and either cut out the shapes for each child or provide scissors for children to cut out the shapes.
1. Have children cut the shapes out of the construction paper copy of the page, if not already done so.
2. Ask: Can you fold the square to show matching parts? Show children one way to fold the square. Show how the parts match. Have them draw a line on the first square to show matching parts.
3. Have children fold the other squares other ways and draw lines to show matching parts 3 other ways.
4. Have children fold the first triangle and draw a line to show matching parts.
5. Have children try to fold the second triangle. Ask: Can you fold the triangle to show matching parts? No
6. Have children draw a shape that has matching parts.

Intervention Lesson D56   201

Teacher Notes

Ongoing Assessment
Ask: **Does a circle have matching parts?** yes

Error Intervention
If children cannot draw the lines to show matching parts in the Exercises,

then have them trace the figure, cut it out, and fold it.

If You Have More Time
Have children find pictures of objects with matching parts from newspapers and magazines. Have them cut out the pictures, glue them to construction paper, and draw lines to show the matching parts.

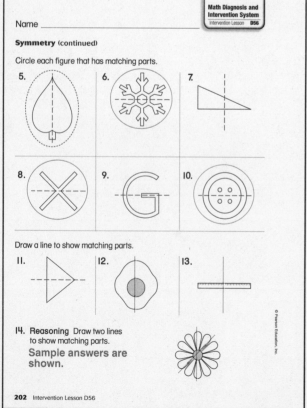

Flat Surfaces and Corners

Name _____

Math Diagnosis and Intervention System

Intervention Lesson **D57**

Flat Surfaces and Corners

Solid	Number of Flat Surfaces	Number of Corners
1. blue	6	8
2. red	2	0
3.	1	0
4. blue	6	8
5.	0	0

Materials: Geometric solids for demonstration, crayons or markers

1. Show children a flat surface on the rectangular prism. Ask: *How many flat surfaces does the solid have?* Have children write 6 in the table.
2. Show a corner on the rectangular prism. Ask: *How many corners does the solid have?* Have children write 8 in the table. Tell children corners are called vertices and one corner is a vertex.
3. Show the cylinder. Ask: *How many flat surfaces does a cylinder have?* Have children write 2 in the table. Ask: *How many corners does it have?* Have children write 0 in the table.
4. Do the other solids similarly.
5. Have children solve some riddles. Say: *I have two flat surfaces and roll. Which solid am I?* Have children color the cylinder red.
6. Say: *I have 8 corners and cannot roll. Which solid am I?* Have children color the rectangular prism and the cube blue.

Intervention Lesson D57 **203**

© Pearson Education, Inc.

Teacher Notes

Ongoing Assessment
Ask children to show a corner or flat surface on one of the geometric solids.

Error Intervention
If children cannot tell whether or not solids roll,

then use D49: Solid Figures.

If You Have More Time
Show pairs of solids and have children tell how they are alike and how they are different.

Name _____

Math Diagnosis and Intervention System

Intervention Lesson **D57**

Flat Surfaces and Corners (continued)

Color the figure that follows the rule.

6. 1 flat surface
   no corners

7. 6 flat surfaces
   does not roll

8. no flat surfaces
   no corners

9. 2 flat surfaces
   rolls

10. 6 flat surfaces
    8 corners

11. **Reasoning** What rule tells how these
    solid figures are alike?

    flat surfaces, roll

© Pearson Education, Inc.

204 Intervention Lesson D57

Faces, Corners, and Edges

Name _____

Faces, Corners, and Edges

	Solid	Number of Flat Surfaces	Number of Edges	Number of Vertices
1.	rectangular prism	6	12	8
2.	cylinder	2	0	0
3.	cone	1	0	0
4.	pyramid	5	8	5
5.	sphere	0	0	0
6.	cube	6	12	8

Materials: Geometric solids for demonstration

1. Show children a flat surface on the rectangular prism. Ask: *How many flat surfaces does the solid have?* Have children write 6 in the table. Tell children flat surfaces on objects that do not roll are faces. Ask: *Does a cylinder have faces?* no *Does a pyramid have faces?* yes
2. Show an edge on the rectangular prism. Ask: *How many edges does the prism have?* Have them write 12 in the table.
3. Show a corner on the rectangular prism. Ask: *How many corners does the solid have?* Have children write 8 in the table. Tell children corners are called vertices and one corner is a vertex.
4. Show the cylinder. Ask: *How many flat surfaces does a cylinder have?* Have children write 2 in the table. Ask: *How many edges does it have?* Have children write 0 in the table. Ask: *How many vertices does it have?* Have children write 0 in the table.
5. Do the other solids similarly.

Intervention Lesson D58   **205**

Teacher Notes

Ongoing Assessment
Ask children to show a face, vertex, or edge on the pyramid geometric solid.

Error Intervention
If children have trouble with the names of the solids,

then use D49: Solid Figures

If You Have More Time
Have children cut out a picture of an object which is the same shape as one of the solids. Have them write the name of the solid and tell how many flat surfaces, edges, and vertices it has.

Name _____

Faces, Corners, and Edges (continued)

Write the name of the solid. Find how many flat surfaces, corners, and edges.

	Solid	Name	Flat Surfaces	Corners	Edges
7.	VEG SOUP	cylinder	2	0	0
8.		sphere	0	0	0
9.	A B	cube	6	8	12
10.		cone	1	0	0
11.		pyramid	5	5	8

© Pearson Education, Inc.

Solid Figures

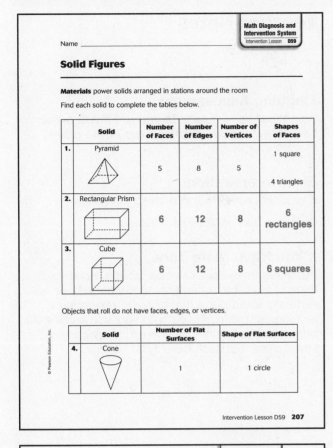

Name _____

Math Diagnosis and Intervention System
Intervention Lesson   **D59**

Solid Figures

Materials power solids arranged in stations around the room

Find each solid to complete the tables below.

	Solid	Number of Faces	Number of Edges	Number of Vertices	Shapes of Faces
1.	Pyramid	5	8	5	1 square 4 triangles
2.	Rectangular Prism	6	12	8	6 rectangles
3.	Cube	6	12	8	6 squares

Objects that roll do not have faces, edges, or vertices.

	Solid	Number of Flat Surfaces	Shape of Flat Surfaces
4.	Cone	1	1 circle

© Pearson Education, Inc.

Intervention Lesson D59   **207**

Name _____

Math Diagnosis and Intervention System
Intervention Lesson   **D59**

Solid Figures (continued)

	Solid	Number of Flat Surfaces	Shape of Flat Surfaces
5.	Cylinder	2	2 circles
6.	Sphere	0	

Name the solid figure that each object looks like.

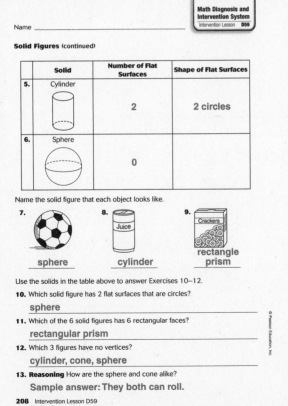

7. sphere

8. cylinder

9. rectangle prism

Use the solids in the table above to answer Exercises 10–12.

10. Which solid figure has 2 flat surfaces that are circles?

sphere

11. Which of the 6 solid figures has 6 rectangular faces?

rectangular prism

12. Which 3 figures have no vertices?

cylinder, cone, sphere

13. **Reasoning** How are the sphere and cone alike?

Sample answer: They both can roll.

© Pearson Education, Inc.

Teacher Notes

Ongoing Assessment

Ask: **Which two solids are the most alike?** Cube and rectangular prism; they have the same number of faces, edges, and vertices.

Error Intervention

If students have trouble naming the shapes of the faces or counting the number of faces, edges, and vertices,

then use D50: Flat Surfaces of Solid Figures, D57: Flat Surfaces and Corners, and D58: Faces, Corners, and Edges.

If You Have More Time

Have a "Solid Bee." Put solids into a bag, including at least one of each discussed in the lesson. Mix in real life objects like a ball, piece of chalk, eraser, and number cube. Have students stand in line. Say: "I need to know the name of this solid." Then pull a solid out of the bag. The first student in line names the solid. If the name is correct, the student goes to the end of the line. If the name is incorrect, the student sits down. Give each student a turn naming a solid. Each round, ask a different question such as:
I need to know how many faces (or flat surfaces) this solid has;
I need to know how many edges this solid has;
I need to know how many vertices this solid has.

Breaking Apart Solids

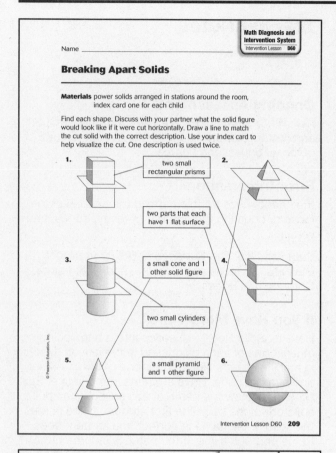

Name _____

Breaking Apart Solids

Materials power solids arranged in stations around the room, index card one for each child

Find each shape. Discuss with your partner what the solid figure would look like if it were cut horizontally. Draw a line to match the cut solid with the correct description. Use your index card to help visualize the cut. One description is used twice.

1.

two small rectangular prisms

2.

two parts that each have 1 flat surface

3.

a small cone and 1 other solid figure

4.

two small cylinders

5.

a small pyramid and 1 other figure

6.

Intervention Lesson D60   **209**

Teacher Notes

Ongoing Assessment
Ask: *What solid figure do you get if you place two cubes together, one on top of the other?* Rectangular prism

Error Intervention
If students have trouble naming the solids,

then use D59 or I1: Solid Figures.

If You Have More Time
Put students in pairs or small groups. Have them think of solid items that are cut horizontally or vertically. Example: a loaf of bread resembles a rectangular prism, it is cut into very thin rectangular prisms; a grapefruit is a sphere, it is typically cut into 2 parts that each have 1 flat surface.

Name _____

Breaking Apart Solids (continued)

Write the letters of the two smaller solids that make up the larger solids in Exercises 7–10.

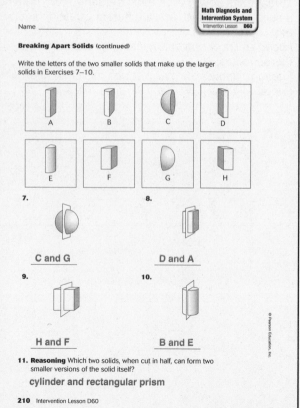

A

B

C

D

E

F

G

H

7.

C and G

8.

D and A

9.

H and F

10.

B and E

11. **Reasoning** Which two solids, when cut in half, can form two smaller versions of the solid itself?

cylinder and rectangular prism

Lines and Line Segments

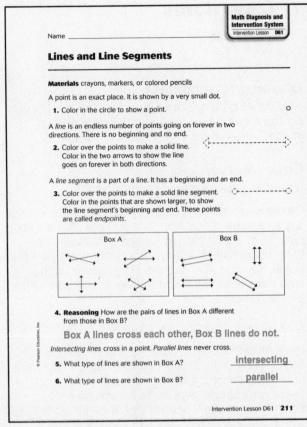

Math Diagnosis and Intervention System
Intervention Lesson   D61

Name _____

Lines and Line Segments

Materials crayons, markers, or colored pencils

A point is an exact place. It is shown by a very small dot.

1. Color in the circle to show a point.

A *line* is an endless number of points going on forever in two directions. There is no beginning and no end.

2. Color over the points to make a solid line. Color in the two arrows to show the line goes on forever in both directions.

A *line segment* is a part of a line. It has a beginning and an end.

3. Color over the points to make a solid line segment. Color in the points that are shown larger, to show the line segment's beginning and end. These points are called *endpoints*.

```
Box A                          Box B
```

4. Reasoning How are the pairs of lines in Box A different from those in Box B?

  Box A lines cross each other, Box B lines do not.

Intersecting lines cross in a point. *Parallel lines* never cross.

5. What type of lines are shown in Box A?   intersecting

6. What type of lines are shown in Box B?   parallel

Intervention Lesson D61   **211**

© Pearson Education, Inc.

Teacher Notes

Ongoing Assessment
Ask: *Why should teachers say "Please get in a line segment." instead of "Please get in a line"?* When students line up there is a beginning and an end. A line goes on forever in both directions.

Error Intervention
If students confuse parallel and intersecting lines,

then show students that the two L's in the word parallel never cross. So lines that never cross are parallel.

If You Have More Time
Put students in pairs. Give each a copy of a city or neighborhood map. Maps can be printed from the internet. Have students take turns identifying streets that are parallel to each other and ones that intersect.

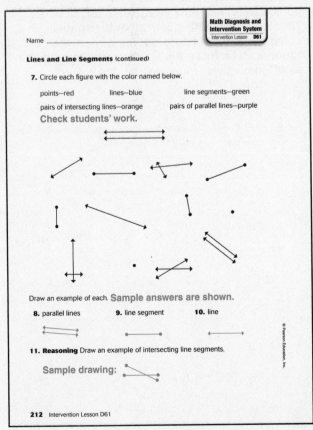

Math Diagnosis and Intervention System
Intervention Lesson   D61

Name _____

Lines and Line Segments (continued)

7. Circle each figure with the color named below.

points—red   lines—blue   line segments—green

pairs of intersecting lines—orange   pairs of parallel lines—purple

Check students' work.

Draw an example of each. **Sample answers are shown.**

8. parallel lines   **9.** line segment   **10.** line

11. Reasoning Draw an example of intersecting line segments.

Sample drawing:

© Pearson Education, Inc.

212 Intervention Lesson D61

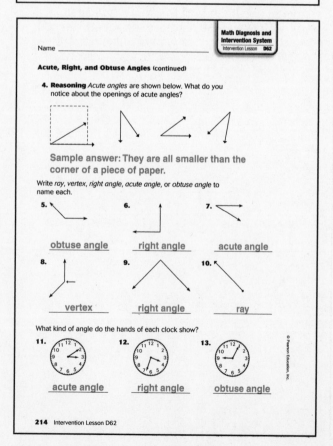

Name _____

**Math Diagnosis and
Intervention System**
Intervention Lesson   **D62**

Acute, Right, and Obtuse Angles

Materials 1 inch square piece of paper for each student,
crayons or markers

A *ray* is part of a line. The endpoint is the beginning
of the ray, and the arrow shows it goes on forever.

An *angle* is made by two rays that have the same
endpoint. That endpoint is called the *vertex*.

1. Color each ray of the angle at the
   right, a different color.

   Check student's coloring

Place a side of your square on one ray, and the corner on the
vertex for each angle in 2 to 4.

2. **Reasoning** *Right angles* are shown below. What do you
   notice about the openings of right angles?

   Sample answer: They are the same size as the
   corner of a piece of paper.

3. **Reasoning** *Obtuse angles* are shown below. What do you notice about
   the openings of obtuse angles?

   Sample answer: They are all larger than the corner
   of a piece of paper.

Intervention Lesson D62   **213**

Name _____

**Math Diagnosis and
Intervention System**
Intervention Lesson   **D62**

Acute, Right, and Obtuse Angles (continued)

4. **Reasoning** *Acute angles* are shown below. What do you
   notice about the openings of acute angles?

   Sample answer: They are all smaller than the
   corner of a piece of paper.

Write *ray, vertex, right angle, acute angle,* or *obtuse angle* to
name each.

5.   obtuse angle   6.   right angle   7.   acute angle

8.   vertex   9.   right angle   10.   ray

What kind of angle do the hands of each clock show?

11.   acute angle   12.   right angle   13.   obtuse angle

214 Intervention Lesson D62

Teacher Notes

Ongoing Assessment

Ask: *What type of angle is formed by the hands
on the clock when it shows the time school
starts?* Answer will vary by school start times.

Error Intervention

If students confuse acute and obtuse,

then help students by telling them that people often
say to a baby "Look how little you are. You are so
cute." So, a little baby is "acute". This will help
them remember that acute is smaller than a right
angle. You can also say the word "acute" with a
small, squeaky voice and the word "obtuse" with a
big, burly voice.

If You Have More Time

Have students play a math version of "Simon
Says". Have a student be Simon, stand in the front
of the class room, and say statements such as the
following: "Simon says make an obtuse angle."
Students can show acute, right, and obtuse angles
with both arms. They can also show a ray by
pointing with one arm extended in any direction.
Those who correctly make an obtuse angle
continue. Those who do not must sit down.
Students who make the figure when Simon doesn't
say "Simon says" must also sit down.

Polygons

Name _____

Math Diagnosis and
Intervention System
Intervention Lesson   **D63**

Polygons

Box A	Box B

1. The figures in Box A are polygons. The figures in Box B are not. How are the figures in Box A different from those in Box B?

Answers will vary.

To be a polygon:

- All sides must be made of straight line segments.
- Line segments must only intersect at a vertex.
- The figure must be closed.

Polygons are named by the number of sides each has. Complete the table.

	Shape	Number of Sides	Number of Vertices	Name
2.		3	3	Triangle
3.		4	4	Quadrilateral
4.		5	5	Pentagon
5.		6	6	Hexagon
6.		8	8	Octagon

© Pearson Education, Inc.

Intervention Lesson D63   **215**

Name _____

Math Diagnosis and
Intervention System
Intervention Lesson   **D63**

Polygons (continued)

Tell if each figure is a polygon. Write *yes* or *no*.

7.   no

8.   yes

9.   no

Name each polygon. Then tell the number of sides and the number of vertices each polygon has.

10.   hexagon; 6, 6

11.   pentagon; 5, 5

12.   triangle; 3, 3

13.   quadrilateral; 4, 4

14.   octagon; 8, 8

15.   quadrilateral; 4, 4

16. Reasoning What is the least number of sides a polygon can have?   3 sides

17. Reasoning A regular polygon is a polygon with all sides the same length. Circle the figure on the right that is a regular polygon.

© Pearson Education, Inc.

Teacher Notes

Ongoing Assessment

Ask: *Why is a circle not a polygon?* A polygon must have sides that are line segments. A circle has no line segments.

Error Intervention

If students count the same vertex or side twice,

then have them put an x on each side or vertex as they count it. This will help students to avoid counting a vertex or side more than once.

If You Have More Time

Have students make polygon books. Give each student 3 half-sheets of white paper. With all 3 sheets together, have them fold the papers to make a book. Students should title their book with something having to do with polygons. The first two-page spread should have the heading "Triangles." Let the students use crayons or markers to draw examples of different types of triangles. Also, let them print pictures from the internet or cut out pictures from magazines. Make other two-page spreads for quadrilaterals, pentagons, hexagons, and octagons. The cover, made with construction paper, can be a picture drawn by using only polygons.

Classifying Triangles Using Sides and Angles

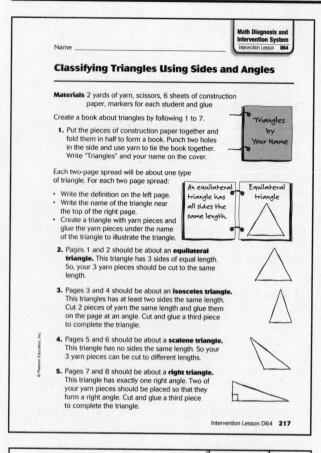

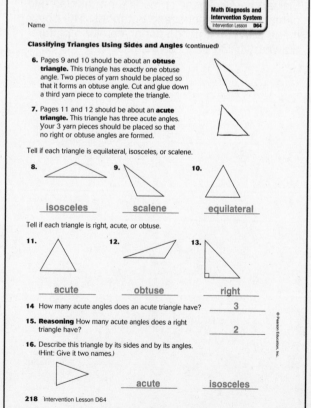

Teacher Notes

Ongoing Assessment

Ask: *What type of angles are in an equilateral triangle?* acute

Error Intervention

If students have trouble identifying right angles, acute angles, and obtuse angles,

then use I4: Acute, Right, and Obtuse Angles.

If You Have More Time

Have students draw a triangle. Trade with a partner and have the partner identify the triangle by its sides and then by its angles.

Quadrilaterals

Worksheet Page 219

Name _____

Quadrilaterals

Materials Have quadrilateral power shapes available for students who want to use them.

For 1 to 5 study each quadrilateral with your partner. Identify the types of angles. Compare the lengths of the sides. Then draw a line to match the quadrilateral with the best description. Descriptions can be used only once.

1. Trapezoid

| Four right angles and all four sides the same length |

2. Parallelogram

| All sides are the same length |

3. Rectangle

| Exactly one pair of parallel sides |

4. Square

| Two pairs of parallel sides |

5. Rhombus

| Four right angles and opposite sides the same length |

6. **Reasoning** What quadrilateral has four right angles and opposite sides the same length, and can also be called a rectangle?   **square**

7. **Reasoning** What quadrilaterals have two pairs of parallel sides, and can also be called parallelograms?
   rectangle, rhombus, square

Intervention Lesson D65   **219**

© Pearson Education, Inc.

Worksheet Page 220

Name _____

Quadrilaterals (continued)

For Exercises 8–13, circle squares red, rectangles blue, parallelograms green, rhombuses orange and trapezoids purple. Some quadrilaterals may be circled more than once.
See teachers note page.

8.   9.   10.

11.   12.   13.

14. I have two pairs of parallel sides, and all of my sides are equal, but I have no right angles. What quadrilateral am I?   **rhombus**

15. I have two pairs of parallel sides and 4 right angles, but all 4 of my sides are not equal. What quadrilateral am I?   **rectangle**

16. Name all of the quadrilaterals in the picture at the right.
    rectangle, rhombus, parallelogram, trapezoid

17. **Reasoning** Why is the quadrilateral on the right a parallelogram, but not a rectangle?
    Sample answer: Both a rectangle and a parallelogram have opposite sides parallel. A rectangle must also have four right angles. This quadrilateral does not have four right angles, so it is a parallelogram, but not a rectangle.

220 Intervention Lesson D65

© Pearson Education, Inc.

Teacher Notes

Ongoing Assessment

Ask: *Are all squares rectangles?* yes *Are all rectangles squares?* no

Error Intervention

If students list only one name for rectangles, squares, or rhombuses,

then ask students leading questions so they can discover that other quadrilateral name(s) can also be used.

If You Have More Time

Put students in pairs. Each pair needs five index cards labeled square, rectangle, rhombus, trapezoid, and parallelogram. Have one student shuffle and draw a card. Both students then need to draw an example of the quadrilateral. Students should compare drawings. Tell them to describe the different ways a quadrilateral can be drawn. Help students to discover that quadrilaterals may be different sizes, but they will always have their specific characteristics.

In items 8–13, each quadrilateral should be circled with the color listed below

8. red, blue, green and orange

9. purple

10. green

11. blue, green

12. orange, green

13. purple

Congruent Figures and Motions

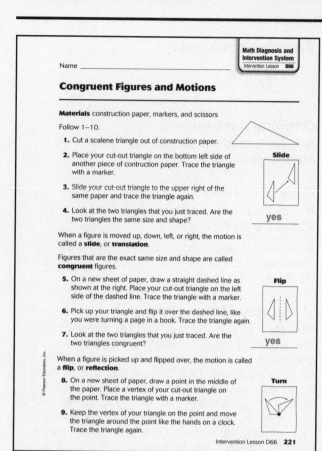

Name _____

Congruent Figures and Motions

Materials construction paper, markers, and scissors

Follow 1–10.

1. Cut a scalene triangle out of construction paper.

2. Place your cut-out triangle on the bottom left side of another piece of contruction paper. Trace the triangle with a marker.

3. Slide your cut-out triangle to the upper right of the same paper and trace the triangle again.

4. Look at the two triangles that you just traced. Are the two triangles the same size and shape?   **yes**

When a figure is moved up, down, left, or right, the motion is called a **slide**, or **translation**.

Figures that are the exact same size and shape are called **congruent** figures.

5. On a new sheet of paper, draw a straight dashed line as shown at the right. Place your cut-out triangle on the left side of the dashed line. Trace the triangle with a marker.

6. Pick up your triangle and flip it over the dashed line, like you were turning a page in a book. Trace the triangle again.

7. Look at the two triangles that you just traced. Are the two triangles congruent?   **yes**

When a figure is picked up and flipped over, the motion is called a **flip**, or **reflection**.

8. On a new sheet of paper, draw a point in the middle of the paper. Place a vertex of your cut-out triangle on the point. Trace the triangle with a marker.

9. Keep the vertex of your triangle on the point and move the triangle around the point like the hands on a clock. Trace the triangle again.

Intervention Lesson D66 **221**

Teacher Notes

Ongoing Assessment

Ask: *Why are all squares not congruent?*
Congruent figures must have the same size and shape. Squares can be different sizes.

Error Intervention

If students have trouble understanding congruency,

then use D54: Same Size, Same Shape.

If students have trouble differentiating between slides, flips, and turns,

then use D55: Ways to Move Shapes.

If students understand congruency, but have trouble deciding if two figures are congruent,

then have students trace one of the figures and place the tracing over the other figure to see if it has the same size and shape.

If You Have More Time

Have students write their name using letters that have been flipped, turned, or slid. Exchange with a partner and have the partner identify what motion was used on each letter. Show the students that some letters can look like a slide and a flip. For example, the letter "I" looks the same when it is flipped and slid to the right.

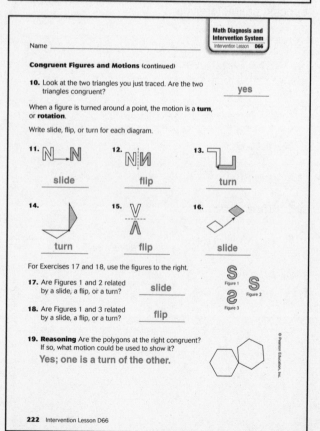

Name _____

Congruent Figures and Motions (continued)

10. Look at the two triangles you just traced. Are the two triangles congruent?   **yes**

When a figure is turned around a point, the motion is a **turn**, or **rotation**.

Write slide, flip, or turn for each diagram.

11.   **slide**

12.   **flip**

13.   **turn**

14.   **turn**

15.   **flip**

16.   **slide**

For Exercises 17 and 18, use the figures to the right.

17. Are Figures 1 and 2 related by a slide, a flip, or a turn?   **slide**

18. Are Figures 1 and 3 related by a slide, a flip, or a turn?   **flip**

19. **Reasoning** Are the polygons at the right congruent? If so, what motion could be used to show it?

Yes; one is a turn of the other.

222 Intervention Lesson D66

Line Symmetry

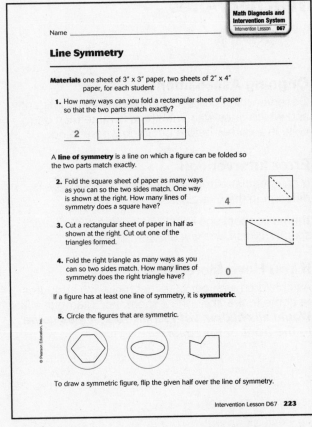

Name _____

Math Diagnosis and Intervention System
Intervention Lesson   **D67**

Line Symmetry

Materials one sheet of 3″ x 3″ paper, two sheets of 2″ x 4″ paper, for each student

1. How many ways can you fold a rectangular sheet of paper so that the two parts match exactly?

   2

A **line of symmetry** is a line on which a figure can be folded so the two parts match exactly.

2. Fold the square sheet of paper as many ways as you can so the two sides match. One way is shown at the right. How many lines of symmetry does a square have?

   4

3. Cut a rectangular sheet of paper in half as shown at the right. Cut out one of the triangles formed.

4. Fold the right triangle as many ways as you can so two sides match. How many lines of symmetry does the right triangle have?

   0

If a figure has at least one line of symmetry, it is **symmetric**.

5. Circle the figures that are symmetric.

To draw a symmetric figure, flip the given half over the line of symmetry.

Intervention Lesson D67   **223**

Name _____

Math Diagnosis and Intervention System
Intervention Lesson   **D67**

Line Symmetry (continued)

Complete the figure below to make a symmetric figure by answering 6 to 8.

6. Find a vertex that is not on the line of symmetry. Count the number of spaces from the line of symmetry to the vertex.

7. Count the same number of spaces on the other side of the line of symmetry and mark a point.

8. Use line segments to connect the new vertices. Do this until the figure is complete.

line of symmetry

2 spaces   2 spaces

Decide whether or not each figure is symmetric. Write Yes or No

9.

   yes

10.

   yes

11.

   no

Complete each figure so the dotted line segment is the line of symmetry.

12.

13.

Draw all lines of symmetry for each figure.

14.

15.

Teacher Notes

Ongoing Assessment

Ask: ***Do you have letters in your name that are symmetrical? If so, which ones?*** Answers will vary depending on name and handwriting style.

Error Intervention

If students have trouble drawing symmetrical figures,

then use D56: Symmetry.

If students have difficulty visualizing the folding to check for symmetry,

then encourage students to trace and cut out the figure to see if the figure is symmetrical.

If You Have More Time

Give the students a few minutes to look around the room and list as many objects as they can that are symmetrical. Have students share their findings. Help them to discover objects that are not obvious, such as the hand on a clock, has a line of symmetry.

Sorting and Classifying

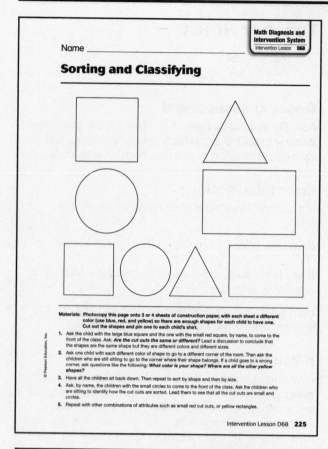

Name _____

Math Diagnosis and Intervention System
Intervention Lesson   **D68**

Sorting and Classifying

Materials: Photocopy this page onto 3 or 4 sheets of construction paper, with each sheet a different color (use blue, red, and yellow) so there are enough shapes for each child to have one. Cut out the shapes and pin one to each child's shirt.

1. Ask the child with the large blue square and the one with the small red square, by name, to come to the front of the class. Ask: *Are the cut outs the same or different?* Lead a discussion to conclude that the shapes are the same shape but they are different colors and different sizes.

2. Ask one child with each different color of shape to go to a different corner of the room. Then ask the children who are still sitting to go to the corner where their shape belongs. If a child goes to a wrong corner, ask questions like the following: *What color is your shape? Where are all the other yellow shapes?*

3. Have all the children sit back down. Then repeat to sort by shape and then by size.

4. Ask, by name, the children with the small circles to come to the front of the class. Ask the children who are sitting to identify how the cut outs are sorted. Lead them to see that all the cut outs are small and circles.

5. Repeat with other combinations of attributes such as small red cut outs, or yellow rectangles.

Intervention Lesson D68   **225**

Teacher Notes

Ongoing Assessment

Observe which children sort themselves confidently and which ones wait until there is more than one child in a corner before deciding where to go.

Error Intervention

If children have trouble choosing which shape is different in the Exercises,

then ask questions like: *Which one has a different shape? Which one is a different size?*

If You Have More Time

Ask children with cut outs that have two attributes to come to the front of the room. For example, ask: *Would all children with small, red shapes come to the front of the room?*

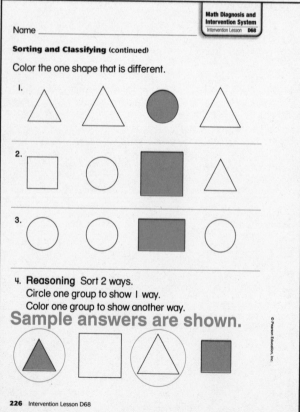

Name _____

Math Diagnosis and Intervention System
Intervention Lesson   **D68**

Sorting and Classifying (continued)

Color the one shape that is different.

1.

2.

3.

4. **Reasoning** Sort 2 ways.
   Circle one group to show I way.
   Color one group to show another way.

Sample answers are shown.

226   Intervention Lesson D68

Graphing

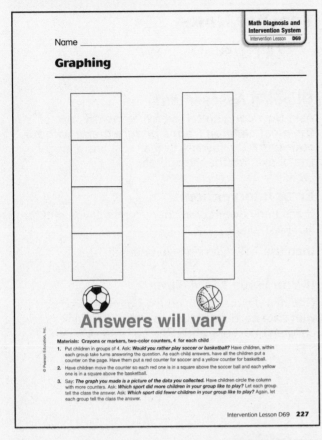

Teacher Notes

Ongoing Assessment

Ask: *How could you find out whether more people in your group like the zoo or the science museum?* See if children can describe the process used in the activity for collecting the data and making the graph.

Error Intervention

If children have trouble choosing which has more or fewer,

then use A2: More and Fewer.

If You Have More Time

Have children collect data and make a graph to find whether children in their group like to watch ice skating or baseball.

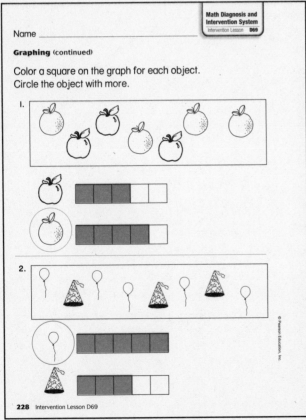

Reading Picture Graphs

Student Page (top)

Reading Picture Graphs

Favorite Shapes   Each shape is 1 choice.

| △ Triangle | △ | △ | △ |
| ○ Circle | ○ | ○ | |

1. How many △ ? 4

2. How many ○ ? 2

3. (△) ○

Favorite Movies

Science Fiction 🚀	☺☺☺☺☺
Animal 🐕	☺☺☺
Comedy 🤡	☺☺☺☺☺☺

4. How many? 🚀 5   5. How many 🤡 ? 6

6. 🚀   🐕   (🤡)

1. Ask children to look at the first graph. Tell them it is a picture graph of favorite shapes and each shape in the graph shows that 1 child chose that shape. Ask: **How many children chose the triangle?** Have children trace the 4.
2. Ask: **How many chose the circle?** Have children write 2.
3. Ask: **Which shape did more children choose?** Have children circle the triangle.
4. Ask children to look at the second graph. Tell them it is a picture graph of favorite types of movies: Science Fiction, Animal, and Comedy. Tell them each stick figure means 1 child chose that type of movie. Ask: **How many children chose Science Fiction?** Have children write 5.
5. Ask **How many chose Comedy?** Have children write 6.
6. Ask: **What type of movie did the most children choose?** Have children circle the cartoon character.

© Pearson Education, Inc.

Intervention Lesson D70 **229**

Student Page (bottom)

Reading Picture Graphs (continued)

Use the graph to answer Exercises 7 to 12.

Favorite Frozen-Yogurt Flavor

Lemon 🍋	🍦🍦🍦🍦
Banana 🍌	🍦🍦🍦
Strawberry 🍓	🍦🍦🍦🍦🍦🍦🍦

7. How many like 🍌 best?   8. How many like 🍓 best?

   3   7

9. Which flavor did 4 children choose?

   🍋   🍌   🍓

10. Which flavor is the favorite of the most?

    🍋   🍌   (🍓)

11. Which flavor is the favorite of the least?

    🍋   (🍌)   🍓

12. How many more chose 🍓 than 🍋 ? 3

© Pearson Education, Inc.

Teacher Notes

Ongoing Assessment

Ask: **How can you tell which is the favorite of the most children from a picture graph without counting?** The favorite of the most has a longer line of pictures than the others.

Error Intervention

If children have trouble choosing the favorite of the least or most,

then use A12: Ordering Numbers to 12.

If You Have More Time

Create a picture graph on the board or overhead with data collected from the class. Then ask children questions about it.

© Pearson Education, Inc.

Reading Bar Graphs

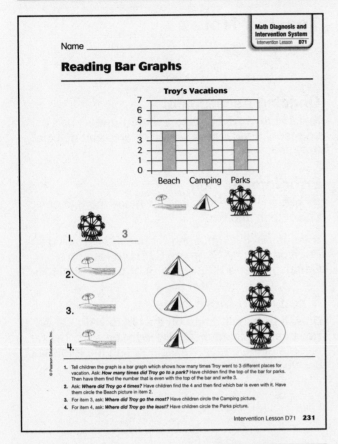

Name _____

Reading Bar Graphs

Troy's Vacations

Beach   Camping   Parks

1. _3_

2.

3.

4.

1. Tell children the graph is a bar graph which shows how many times Troy went to 3 different places for vacation. Ask: *How many times did Troy go to a park?* Have children find the top of the bar for parks. Then have them find the number that is even with the top of the bar and write 3.
2. Ask: *Where did Troy go 4 times?* Have children find the 4 and then find which bar is even with it. Have them circle the Beach picture in item 2.
3. For item 3, ask: *Where did Troy go the most?* Have children circle the Camping picture.
4. For item 4, ask: *Where did Troy go the least?* Have children circle the Parks picture.

Intervention Lesson D71   **231**

Teacher Notes

Ongoing Assessment

Ask: *How can you tell which is the least by just looking at a bar graph?* See which bar is the shortest.

Error Intervention

If children have trouble reading the scale on the bar graph in the Exercises,

then let them count how many squares are shaded after each category.

If You Have More Time

Create a picture graph on the board or overhead with data collected from the class. Then ask children questions about it.

Name _____

Reading Bar Graphs (continued)

Use the bar graph for Exercises 5 to 9.

Favorite Fruit

Apple
Banana
Orange

0 1 2 3 4 5 6 7 8
Number of Children

5. How many chose apples? _7_

6. Which did 5 choose?

7. Which was chosen by the most?

8. Which was chosen by the least?

9. How many more chose apple than orange? _4_

Tallying Results

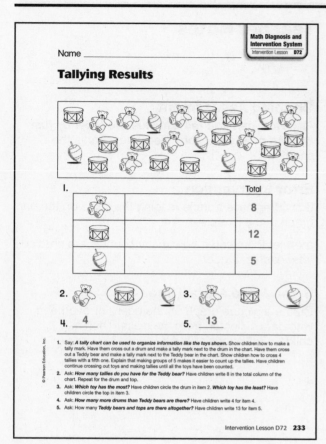

Tallying Results

1.

		Total
(Teddy bear)		8
(drum)		12
(top)		5

2. (Teddy bear) (drum) (top)   3. (Teddy bear) (drum) (top)

4. 4   5. 13

1. Say: *A tally chart can be used to organize information like the toys shown.* Show children how to make a tally mark. Have them cross out a drum and make a tally mark next to the drum in the chart. Have them cross out a Teddy bear and make a tally mark next to the Teddy bear in the chart. Show children how to cross 4 tallies with a fifth one. Explain that making groups of 5 makes it easier to count up the tallies. Have children continue crossing out toys and making tallies until all the toys have been counted.
2. Ask: *How many tallies do you have for the Teddy bear?* Have children write 8 in the total column of the chart. Repeat for the drum and top.
3. Ask: *Which toy has the most?* Have children circle the drum in item 2. *Which toy has the least?* Have children circle the top in item 3.
4. Ask: *How many more drums than Teddy bears are there?* Have children write 4 for item 4.
5. Ask: How many *Teddy bears and tops are there altogether?* Have children write 13 for item 5.

Teacher Notes

Ongoing Assessment
Make sure children make a one-to-one correspondence between tally marks and objects they cross out.

Error Intervention
If children incorrectly find how many more of one object than another,

then use B18: Comparing Stories, B24: Thinking Addition to 12 to Subtract, B33: Stories about Comparing, and B39: Using Subtraction Strategies.

If You Have More Time
Draw a blank tally chart on the board with 3 toys. Have each child make a tally mark by his or her favorite of the 3 toys. As a class, find the totals and answer questions about the chart.

Tallying Results (continued)

For Exercises 6 to 10, use the picture at the right.

6. Make tally marks to show how many of each there are. Then write each total.

		Total
(cup)		9
(plate)		6
(spoon)		14

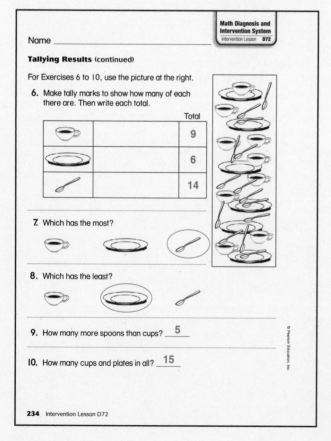

7. Which has the most?

(cup)   (plate)   (spoon)

8. Which has the least?

(cup)   (plate)   (spoon)

9. How many more spoons than cups? 5

10. How many cups and plates in all? 15

Real Graphs

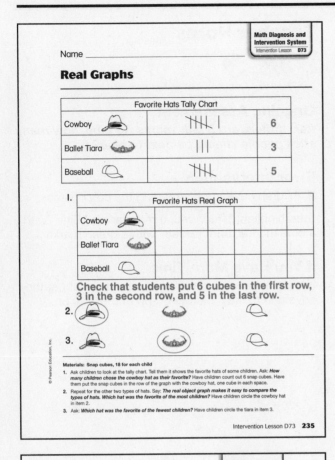

Name _____

Math Diagnosis and
Intervention System
Intervention Lesson **D73**

Real Graphs

Favorite Hats Tally Chart			
Cowboy		𝖳𝖧𝖫 𝖨	6
Ballet Tiara		𝖨𝖨𝖨	3
Baseball		𝖳𝖧𝖫	5

I.

Favorite Hats Real Graph							
Cowboy							
Ballet Tiara							
Baseball							

Check that students put 6 cubes in the first row,
3 in the second row, and 5 in the last row.

2.

3.

Materials: Snap cubes, 18 for each child

1. Ask children to look at the tally chart. Tell them it shows the favorite hats of some children. Ask: *How many children chose the cowboy hat as their favorite?* Have children count out 6 snap cubes. Have them put the snap cubes in the row of the graph with the cowboy hat, one cube in each space.

2. Repeat for the other two types of hats. Say: *The real object graph makes it easy to compare the types of hats. Which hat was the favorite of the most children?* Have children circle the cowboy hat in item 2.

3. Ask: *Which hat was the favorite of the fewest children?* Have children circle the tiara in item 3.

Intervention Lesson D73 **235**

Name _____

Math Diagnosis and
Intervention System
Intervention Lesson **D73**

Real Graphs (continued)

Use the tally chart to make a graph with cubes.

Animals Holly Saw at the Zoo Tally Chart			
Elephant		𝖨𝖨𝖨𝖨	4
Giraffe		𝖨𝖨𝖨	3
Monkey		𝖳𝖧𝖫	5

4.

Animals Holly Saw at the Zoo Real Graph					
Elephant					
Giraffe					
Monkey					

Check that
students
put 4 cubes
in the first
row, 3 in the
second row,
and 5 in the
last row.

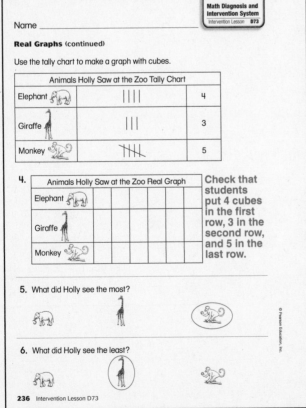

5. What did Holly see the most?

6. What did Holly see the least?

236 Intervention Lesson D73

© Pearson Education, Inc.

Teacher Notes

Ongoing Assessment

Observe whether children use the number to find least and most or if they do it visually from the graph.

Error Intervention

If children do not understand the tally chart,

then use D72: Tallying Results.

If You Have More Time

Have children collect data about their favorite types of hat and use the data to make a real graph.

Data and Picture Graphs

Math Diagnosis and Intervention System
Intervention Lesson D74

Name ____________________

Math Diagnosis and Intervention System
Intervention Lesson D74

Data and Picture Graphs

1.

Favorite Color Tally Chart		
Red	Answers will vary.	
Blue		
Green		

2.

Favorite Color Picture Graph						
Red						
Blue						
Green						

Each is 1 choice.

3. Most? ________

1. Form groups of 6 to 8 children. Ask: ***Which color do you like the most, red, blue, or green?*** Have children in each group take turns answering the question. As each child answers, have all the children in the group make a tally mark in the correct row of the tally chart.
2. Have children total the tallies and write the number in the chart.
3. Have children draw stick people in the first row of the picture graph. Tell them to draw one stick person for each tally mark next to red.
4. Have children do the same for blue and green.
5. Ask: ***Which color was the favorite of the most children in your group?*** Have children write the name of the color.

Name ____________________

Math Diagnosis and Intervention System
Intervention Lesson D74

Data and Picture Graphs (continued)

4. Use tally chart to make a picture graph.

Our Pets Tally Chart		
Dog 	𝍸 I	6
Cat 	IIII	4
Fish 	II	2

Our Pets Picture Graph	
Dog	
Cat	
Fish	

5. Which pet has the most? dog

6. Which pet has the least? fish

Teacher Notes

Ongoing Assessment

Ask: ***If there are 5 tally marks for blue, how many stick people should be next to blue?*** 5

Error Intervention

If children have trouble reading the color names,

then highlight "Red" with a red marker, "Blue" with a blue marker, and "Green" with a green marker.

If You Have More Time

Have children ask classmates what type of pet they have and make a picture graph of the results.

Making Bar Graphs

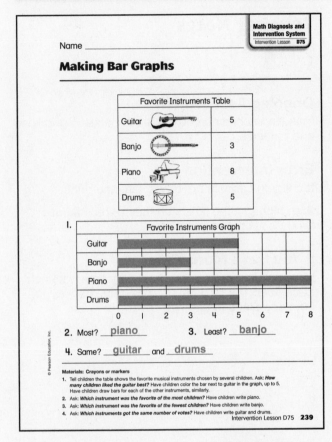

Name _____

Making Bar Graphs

Favorite Instruments Table		
Guitar		5
Banjo		3
Piano		8
Drums		5

1.

| Favorite Instruments Graph |
| Guitar |
| Banjo |
| Piano |
| Drums |

0 1 2 3 4 5 6 7 8

2. Most? __piano__   3. Least? __banjo__

4. Same? __guitar__ and __drums__

Materials: Crayons or markers
1. Tell children the table shows the favorite musical instruments chosen by several children. Ask: *How many children liked the guitar best?* Have children color the bar next to guitar in the graph, up to 5. Have children draw bars for each of the other instruments, similarly.
2. Ask: *Which instrument was the favorite of the most children?* Have children write piano.
3. Ask: *Which instrument was the favorite of the fewest children?* Have children write banjo.
4. Ask: *Which instruments got the same number of votes?* Have children write guitar and drums.

Intervention Lesson D75   **239**

Name _____

Making Bar Graphs (continued)

5. Use the table to make a bar graph.

How We Get to School Table	
Bus	7
Car	3
Walk	5
Bike	4

How We Get to School Graph

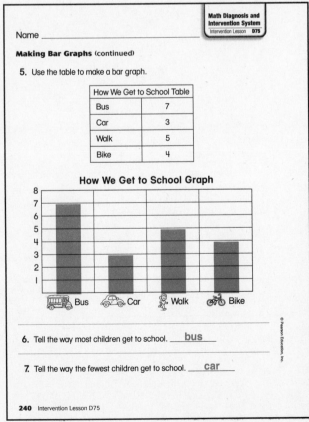

8
7
6
5
4
3
2
1

Bus   Car   Walk   Bike

6. Tell the way most children get to school. __bus__

7. Tell the way the fewest children get to school. __car__

© Pearson Education, Inc.

240 Intervention Lesson D75

Teacher Notes

Ongoing Assessment

Ask: *How did you know how long to make the bar for the banjo?* Since 3 people chose the banjo, color over to the line with 3.

Error Intervention

If children do not understand bar graphs,

then use D71: Reading Bar Graphs.

If You Have More Time

Take a survey of the class about their favorite musical instruments or how they get to school. Have children make a bar graph of the results.

Locations on a Grid

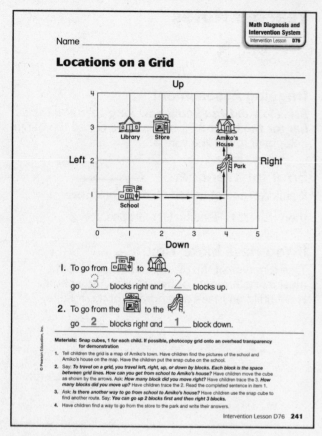

Name _____

Locations on a Grid

1. To go from 🏫 to 🏠,

   go __3__ blocks right and __2__ blocks up.

2. To go from the 🏪 to the 🛝,

   go __2__ blocks right and __1__ block down.

Materials: Snap cubes, 1 for each child. If possible, photocopy grid onto an overhead transparency for demonstration

1. Tell children the grid is a map of Amiko's town. Have children find the pictures of the school and Amiko's house on the map. Have the children put the snap cube on the school.

2. Say: *To travel on a grid, you travel left, right, up, or down by blocks. Each block is the space between grid lines.* How can you get from school to Amiko's house? Have children move the cube as shown by the arrows. Ask: *How many block did you move right?* Have children trace the 3. *How many blocks did you move up?* Have children trace the 2. Read the completed sentence in item 1.

3. Ask: *Is there another way to go from school to Amiko's house?* Have children use the snap cube to find another route. Say: *You can go up 2 blocks first and then right 3 blocks.*

4. Have children find a way to go from the store to the park and write their answers.

Intervention Lesson D76   **241**

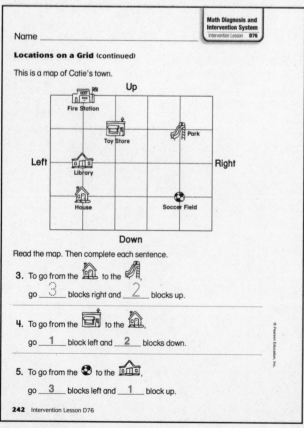

Name _____

Locations on a Grid (continued)

This is a map of Catie's town.

Read the map. Then complete each sentence.

3. To go from the 🏠 to the 🛝,

   go __3__ blocks right and __2__ blocks up.

4. To go from the 🏪 to the 🏠,

   go __1__ block left and __2__ blocks down.

5. To go from the ⚽ to the 🏢,

   go __3__ blocks left and __1__ block up.

242   Intervention Lesson D76

Teacher Notes

Ongoing Assessment
Make sure children count spaces between grid lines and not lines.

Error Intervention
If children confuse up, down, left, and right,

then highlight the labels on their paper and use D47: Position and Location.

If You Have More Time
Have children create and draw a map on one-inch grid paper. Then ask them to describe how to get from one place to another.

Range and Mode

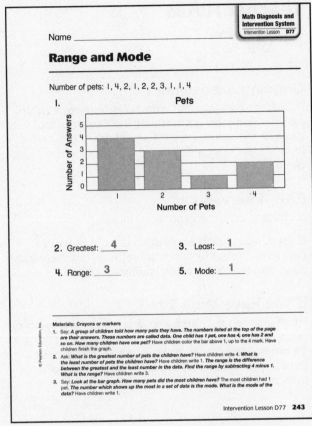

Name _____

Math Diagnosis and
Intervention System
Intervention Lesson **D77**

Range and Mode

Number of pets: 1, 4, 2, 1, 2, 2, 3, 1, 1, 4

1.

Pets

(bar graph with y-axis "Number of Answers" labeled 0–5 and x-axis "Number of Pets" labeled 1, 2, 3, 4)

2. Greatest: __4__   3. Least: __1__

4. Range: __3__   5. Mode: __1__

Materials: Crayons or markers

1. Say: *A group of children told how many pets they have. The numbers listed at the top of the page are their answers. These numbers are called data. One child has 1 pet, one has 4, one has 2 and so on. How many children have one pet?* Have children color the bar above 1, up to the 4 mark. Have children finish the graph.

2. Ask: *What is the greatest number of pets the children have?* Have children write 4. *What is the least number of pets the children have?* Have children write 1. *The range is the difference between the greatest and the least number in the data. Find the range by subtracting 4 minus 1. What is the range?* Have children write 3.

3. Say: *Look at the bar graph. How many pets did the most children have?* The most children had 1 pet. *The number which shows up the most in a set of data is the mode. What is the mode of the data?* Have children write 1.

© Pearson Education, Inc.

Intervention Lesson D77 **243**

© Pearson Education, Inc.

Name _____

Math Diagnosis and
Intervention System
Intervention Lesson **D77**

Range and Mode (continued)

Use the data to answer the questions.
How many stuffed animals do children have?
Room 8 said: 1, 2, 4, 2, 5, 1, 2, 4, 2, 3

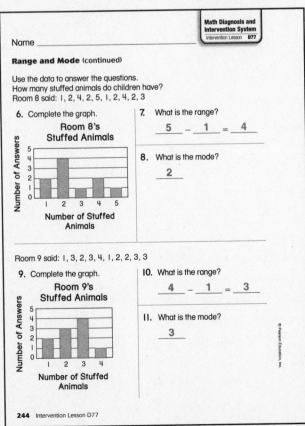

6. Complete the graph.

**Room 8's
Stuffed Animals**

(bar graph with y-axis "Number of Answers" labeled 0–5 and x-axis "Number of Stuffed Animals" labeled 1–5)

7. What is the range?

__5__ – __1__ = __4__

8. What is the mode?

__2__

Room 9 said: 1, 3, 2, 3, 4, 1, 2, 2, 3, 3

9. Complete the graph.

**Room 9's
Stuffed Animals**

(bar graph with y-axis "Number of Answers" labeled 0–5 and x-axis "Number of Stuffed Animals" labeled 1–4)

10. What is the range?

__4__ – __1__ = __3__

11. What is the mode?

__3__

© Pearson Education, Inc.

Teacher Notes

Ongoing Assessment

Ask: *What is the mode of a set of data?* It is the number which shows up the most often. *How does a bar graph help you find the mode?* The mode has the tallest bar.

Error Intervention

If children have trouble making or reading the bar graphs,

then use D71: Reading Bar Graphs and D75: Making Bar Graphs.

If You Have More Time

Collect data from the class on the number of pets or stuffed animals each child has. Then, have children make a bar graph of the data and find the mode and range.

Likely or Unlikely

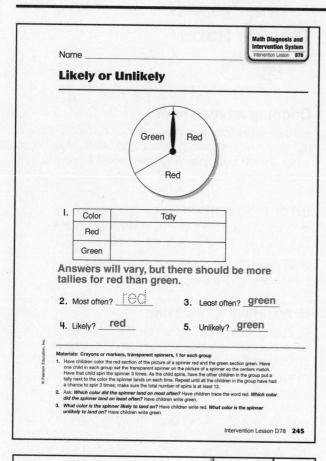

Name _____

Likely or Unlikely

1.

Color	Tally
Red	
Green	

Answers will vary, but there should be more tallies for red than green.

2. Most often? _red_

3. Least often? _green_

4. Likely? _red_

5. Unlikely? _green_

Materials: Crayons or markers, transparent spinners, 1 for each group

1. Have children color the red section of the picture of a spinner red and the green section green. Have one child in each group set the transparent spinner on the picture of a spinner so the centers match. Have that child spin the spinner 3 times. As the child spins, have the other children in the group put a tally next to the color the spinner lands on each time. Repeat until all the children in the group have had a chance to spin 3 times; make sure the total number of spins is at least 12.

2. Ask: *Which color did the spinner land on most often?* Have children trace the word red. *Which color did the spinner land on least often?* Have children write green.

3. *What color is the spinner likely to land on?* Have children write red. *What color is the spinner unlikely to land on?* Have children write green.

Intervention Lesson D78   **245**

Teacher Notes

Ongoing Assessment

Ask: *How can you tell without spinning, which color is likely on a spinner?* The likely color covers more of the spinner. See if any children realize the color must cover more than half of the spinner to be likely.

Error Intervention

If children confuse likely and unlikely,

then explain that if something is likely, it usually happens more often than something that is unlikely. Also, explain that unlikely means *not* likely.

If You Have More Time

Have children put the transparent spinner over one of the pictures of spinners in the Exercises and spin 12 times. Have them make a tally chart and see if the spinner landed on the likely color more often than on the unlikely color.

Name _____

Likely or Unlikely (continued)

Color each spinner.
Circle the color each spinner is **likely** to land on.

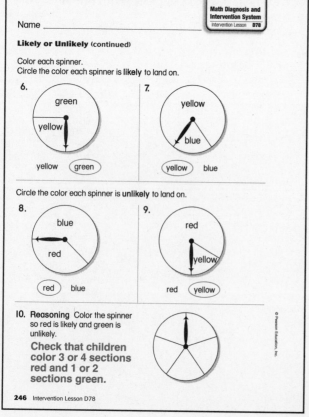

6.
yellow   (green)

7.
yellow   blue

Circle the color each spinner is **unlikely** to land on.

8.
(red)   blue

9.
red   (yellow)

10. **Reasoning** Color the spinner so red is likely and green is unlikely.

   Check that children color 3 or 4 sections red and 1 or 2 sections green.

Certain or Impossible

Name _____

Certain or Impossible

1. [cube]   (certain)
             impossible

2. [cube]   certain
             (impossible)

3. [cube] is certain   [cube] [cube] [cube] [cube] [cube]
    All snap cubes must be blue.

4. [cube] is impossible   [cube] [cube] [cube] [cube] [cube]
    Colors may vary, but none can be yellow.

5. [cube] is impossible   [cube] [cube] [cube] [cube] [cube]
    Colors may vary, but none can be green.

6. [cube] is certain   [cube] [cube] [cube] [cube] [cube]
    All snap cubes must be brown.

Materials: 5 green snap cubes in an opaque bag for each group, crayons or markers

1. Tell children to not look in the bag. Have children in each group take turns pulling a snap cube out of the bag, saying its color, and then putting it back. Have them pass the bag around until every child has had 2 or 3 turns.

2. Ask: *What color snap cube did you get each time?* Have children color the first snap cube green. *If you pull a cube out again, what color would you get?* green; Say: *Pour out the cubes from the bag. You are certain to get a green cube when you pull a cube from the bag.* Have children circle certain.

3. Have children color the second cube yellow. Ask: *Is it possible to get a yellow cube from the bag?* no; Say: *It is impossible to get a yellow cube from the bag.* Have children circle impossible.

4. Have children color the first snap cube in item 3 blue. Ask: *If you are certain to get blue from the bag, what color should the other snap cubes in the bag be?* Have children color the other 5 snap cubes in item 3 blue.

5. Have children color the first snap cube in item 4 yellow. Have them color the other 5 snap cubes to make it impossible to pick yellow.

6. Have children color the first snap cube in item 5 green. Have them color the other 5 snap cubes a different way to make it impossible to pick green.

7. Have children color the first snap cube in item 6 brown. Ask: *If you are certain to get brown from the bag, what color should the other snap cubes in the bag be?* Have children color the other 5 snap cubes in item 6 brown.

© Pearson Education, Inc.

Intervention Lesson D79   **247**

Name _____

Certain or Impossible (continued)

Color the balloons to make each sentence true.

7. You are certain to pick an orange balloon.

   [balloon] [balloon] [balloon] [balloon]   **All balloons must be orange.**

8. It is impossible to pick a yellow balloon.

   [balloon] [balloon] [balloon] [balloon]   **Balloon colors may vary, but none of them may be yellow.**

9. It is impossible to pick a red balloon.

   [balloon] [balloon] [balloon] [balloon]   **Balloon colors may vary, but none of them may be red.**

10. **Reasoning** You are certain to pick a yellow balloon and it is impossible to pick a blue balloon.

    [balloon] [balloon] [balloon] [balloon]   **All balloons must be yellow.**

© Pearson Education, Inc.

248 Intervention Lesson D79

Teacher Notes

Ongoing Assessment

Have children put 5 various colors of snap cubes in a bag, but make sure they do not have any brown snap cubes. Make sure children do not include any brown snap cubes. Ask: *Is it certain or impossible that if you pull a snap cube out of the bag that it will be brown?* impossible

Error Intervention

If children do not understand certain and impossible,

then explain something that is certain *has* to happen; it will happen every time. Something that is impossible cannot happen; it will never happen.

If You Have More Time

Have one child in each group put 5 snap cubes in a bag so a color they choose is certain or impossible. Have the other children in the group take turns pulling cubes from the bag. On each turn, the child tries to guess what color is certain or impossible. The first child says no until the rule is guessed. Continue until each child has a turn putting cubes in the bag.

Certain, Probable, Impossible

Worksheet (page 249)

Name _____

Certain, Probable, Impossible

1.

Color	Tally
Yellow	
Green	
Blue	

Answers will vary, but there should be more tallies on blue than yellow and none on green.

2. Probable?   yellow   green   (blue)

3. Impossible?   yellow   (green)   blue

4. Certain?   (yellow or blue)   blue or green

5. Square
impossible   (probable)   certain

6. Triangle
(impossible)   probable   certain

Materials: 15 snap cubes in an opaque bag for each group, with 12 blue and 3 yellow

1. Tell children not to look in the bag. Have children in each group take turns pulling a snap cube out of the bag, saying its color, and then putting it back. Have all the children in the group make a tally for each color. Have children pass the bag around until there are 30 tallies in the chart.
2. Ask: *What color snap cube did you get most often?* blue *If you pull out another cube what color would you probably get?* blue; Say: *So blue is probable.* Have children circle blue.
3. Ask: *Did you get any green cubes?* no; Have children look at the contents of the bag. *If you keep drawing out cubes, would you ever get any green cubes?* no; Say: *It is impossible to get a green cube.* Have children circle green.
4. Ask: *What colors will you get every time?* You will always get either blue or yellow. Say: *It is certain you will get either blue or yellow.* Have children circle yellow or blue.
5. Say: *Suppose the shapes shown are put in a bag and you pulled one out without looking. Is it impossible, probable, or certain that you draw a square?* Have children circle probable. *Is it impossible, probable, or certain that you draw a triangle?* Have children circle impossible.

Intervention Lesson D80   **249**

Worksheet (page 250)

Name _____

Certain, Probable, Impossible (continued)

Seven shapes are placed in a bag. Is it impossible, probable, or certain that you draw the shape shown? Circle the answer.

7. Circle
(impossible)   probable   certain

8. Rectangle or triangle
impossible   probable   (certain)

9. Rectangle
impossible   (probable)   certain

Eight shapes are placed in a bag. Is it impossible, probable, or certain that you draw the shape shown? Circle the answer.

10. Triangle or circle
impossible   probable   (certain)

11. Circle
impossible   (probable)   certain

12. Square
(impossible)   probable   certain

250   Intervention Lesson D80

Teacher Notes

Ongoing Assessment

Ask: *If a bag has 6 yellow cubes, is it impossible, probable, or certain you will get a yellow cube when you take one out of the bag?* certain

Error Intervention

If children do not know how to make a tally chart,

then use D72: Tallying Results

If children do not understand certain and impossible,

then use D79: Certain or Impossible

If You Have More Time

Put 4 brown and 2 yellow snap cubes in an opaque bag. Have children draw cubes from the bag and make a tally chart of the results. Have them name the color that is probable and a color that is impossible based on the tally chart. Then, let them look in the bag to check their conclusions.

Graphing Ordered Pairs

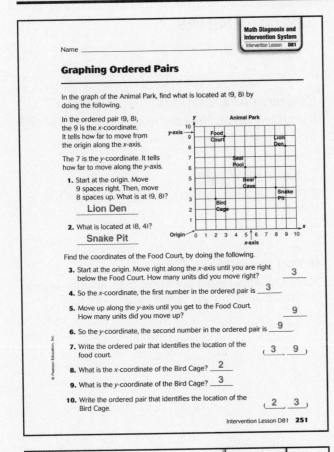

Name _____

Graphing Ordered Pairs

In the graph of the Animal Park, find what is located at (9, 8) by doing the following.

In the ordered pair (9, 8), the 9 is the *x*-coordinate. It tells how far to move from the origin along the *x*-axis.

The 7 is the *y*-coordinate. It tells how far to move along the *y*-axis.

1. Start at the origin. Move 9 spaces right. Then, move 8 spaces up. What is at (9, 8)?
   Lion Den

2. What is located at (8, 4)?
   Snake Pit

Find the coordinates of the Food Court, by doing the following.

3. Start at the origin. Move right along the *x*-axis until you are right below the Food Court. How many units did you move right? **3**

4. So the *x*-coordinate, the first number in the ordered pair is **3**.

5. Move up along the *y*-axis until you get to the Food Court. How many units did you move up? **9**

6. So the *y*-coordinate, the second number in the ordered pair is **9**.

7. Write the ordered pair that identifies the location of the food court. (**3** , **9**)

8. What is the *x*-coordinate of the Bird Cage? **2**

9. What is the *y*-coordinate of the Bird Cage? **3**

10. Write the ordered pair that identifies the location of the Bird Cage. (**2** , **3**)

© Pearson Education, Inc.

Intervention Lesson D81 **251**

Name _____

Graphing Ordered Pairs (continued)

11. **Reasoning** Use the graph of the Animal Park and compare the coordinates of the Seal Pool and the Bear Cave.
   The Seal Pool is at (5, 6) and the Bear Cave is at (6, 5). The numbers are the same, but in different orders.

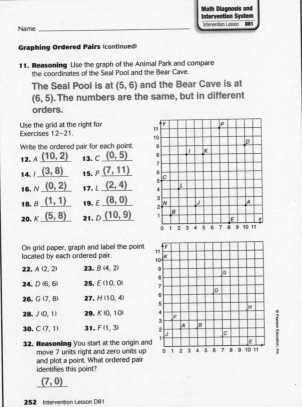

Use the grid at the right for Exercises 12–21.

Write the ordered pair for each point.

12. A **(10, 2)**   13. C **(0, 5)**

14. I **(3, 8)**   15. P **(7, 11)**

16. N **(0, 2)**   17. L **(2, 4)**

18. B **(1, 1)**   19. E **(8, 0)**

20. K **(5, 8)**   21. D **(10, 9)**

On grid paper, graph and label the point located by each ordered pair.

22. A (2, 2)   23. B (4, 2)

24. D (6, 6)   25. E (10, 0)

26. G (7, 8)   27. H (10, 4)

28. J (0, 1)   29. K (0, 10)

30. C (7, 1)   31. F (1, 3)

32. **Reasoning** You start at the origin and move 7 units right and zero units up and plot a point. What ordered pair identifies this point?
   (7, 0)

© Pearson Education, Inc.

252 Intervention Lesson D81

Teacher Notes

Ongoing Assessment
Make sure students count spaces, not lines.

Error Intervention
If students confuse the *x*- and *y*-coordinates,

then state that the first number is always horizontal and the second is always vertical. Use (h, v) to help them remember.

If You Have More Time
Have students work in pairs and play Guess My Location. One partner writes down an ordered pair to chose a point. The second student moves a counter on a coordinate grid, one space at a time. The first student says closer or farther for each move until the second student finds the point. Change roles and repeat, as time allows.

Recording Data from a Survey

Name _____

Recording Data from a Survey

Take a survey by asking, "What is your choice for a classroom mascot: a falcon, a cougar, a stingray, or a bear?" **All answers will vary.**

1. Write each student's answer in the box below.

Choice of Classroom Mascot

2. Make a tally mark for each choice given. Remember, tallies are made in groups of 5 so that they are easier to count.

Sample of 12 Tally Marks

卌 卌 ||

Choice of Classroom Mascot

Mascot	Tally	Total
Falcon		
Cougar		
Stingray		
Bear		

3. Count the tally marks. Record the total for each mascot choice.

4. How many students answered the survey? _____

5. Which mascot was chosen the most? _____

6. Which mascot was chosen the least? _____

Intervention Lesson D82   **253**

Name _____

Recording Data from a Survey (continued)

Favorite Season of the Year

Summer	Fall	Summer	Winter	Spring	Fall
Winter	Summer	Spring	Fall	Fall	Spring
Summer	Winter	Winter	Winter	Summer	Winter

7. Complete the tally chart for the data above.

Favorite Season of the Year

Time of Year	Tally	Total
Spring	|||	3
Summer	卌	5
Fall	||||	4
Winter	卌 |	6

8. What was the question for the survey?
What is your favorite season of the year?

9. How many people answered the survey? _____ 18

10. Which season was the favorite of the most people? Winter

11. Which season was the least favorite of the people? Spring

12. How many more people chose Summer over Spring? 2

13. Reasoning Write the seasons in order from least favorite to most favorite.
Spring, Fall, Summer, Winter

14. Reasoning How many more people would have to have chosen Summer for it to be the most favorite season? 2

Teacher Notes

Ongoing Assessment

Ask: *What would the tally marks look like for 14?*

卌 卌 \|\|\|\|

Error Intervention

If students have trouble with the concept of tally marks,

then use D72: Tallying Results.

If You Have More Time

Have students take a survey of their favorite season and make a tally chart of the data.

Reading and Making Pictographs

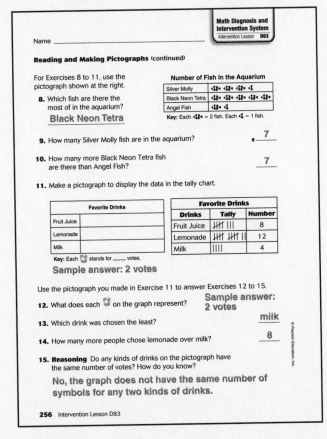

Name _____

**Math Diagnosis and
Intervention System**
Intervention Lesson **D83**

Reading and Making Pictographs

The members of Tom's class voted for their favorite pizza toppings. The results are shown in the tally chart at the right. Answer 1 to 7 to help you make and use a pictograph of the data.

Favorite Pizza Toppings		
Toppings	**Tally**	**Number**
Sausage	IIII	4
Vegetables	III	3
Pepperoni	IIII IIII	10

1. In the first row of the chart below write a title that best describes the pictograph. Then list the three toppings in the first column.

Favorite Pizza Toppings	
Sausage	◯ ◯
Vegetables	◯ ◖
Pepperoni	◯ ◯ ◯ ◯ ◯

Each ◯ = 2 votes.   Each ◖ = __1__ vote.

2. Complete the pictograph key.

3. Decide how many symbols are needed for each topping. Since sausage got 4 votes, draw 2 circles next to sausage. Since vegetables got 3 votes, draw 1 circle and 1 half-circle next to vegetables.

4. How many symbols are needed for pepperoni? **5**

5. Draw 5 circles for pepperoni. Make sure you line up the symbols.

6. Which topping got the greatest number of votes? __pepperoni__

7. Reasoning How can you tell which topping got the greatest number of votes by looking at the pictograph?

The topping with the most number of circles got the greatest number of votes.

Intervention Lesson D83 **255**

© Pearson Education, Inc.

Name _____

**Math Diagnosis and
Intervention System**
Intervention Lesson **D83**

Reading and Making Pictographs (continued)

For Exercises 8 to 11, use the pictograph shown at the right.

8. Which fish are there the most of in the aquarium?

Black Neon Tetra

Number of Fish in the Aquarium	
Silver Molly	◀‖▸ ◀‖▸ ◀‖▸ ◀‖
Black Neon Tetra	◀‖▸ ◀‖▸ ◀‖▸ ◀‖▸ ◀‖
Angel Fish	◀‖▸ ◀‖

Key: Each ◀‖▸ = 2 fish. Each ◀‖ = 1 fish.

9. How many Silver Molly fish are in the aquarium? __7__

10. How many more Black Neon Tetra fish are there than Angel Fish? __7__

11. Make a pictograph to display the data in the tally chart.

Favorite Drinks	
Fruit Juice	
Lemonade	
Milk	

Key: Each ⬛ stands for ____ votes.

Sample answer: 2 votes

Favorite Drinks		
Drinks	**Tally**	**Number**
Fruit Juice	IIII III	8
Lemonade	IIII IIII II	12
Milk	IIII	4

Use the pictograph you made in Exercise 11 to answer Exercises 12 to 15.

12. What does each ⬛ on the graph represent? **Sample answer: 2 votes**

13. Which drink was chosen the least? __milk__

14. How many more people chose lemonade over milk? __8__

15. Reasoning Do any kinds of drinks on the pictograph have the same number of votes? How do you know?

No, the graph does not have the same number of symbols for any two kinds of drinks.

© Pearson Education, Inc.

Teacher Notes

Ongoing Assessment

Ask: *If sausage would have gotten 7 votes, instead of 4, how many circles would you have drawn?* 3 circles and 1 half-circle

Error Intervention

If students have trouble reading pictographs,

then use D70: Reading Picture Graphs.

If students have trouble collecting data and making pictographs,

then use D74: Data and Picture Graphs.

If You Have More Time

Have students take a survey of their favorite pizza toppings and make a pictograph of the data.

Reading and Making a Bar Graph

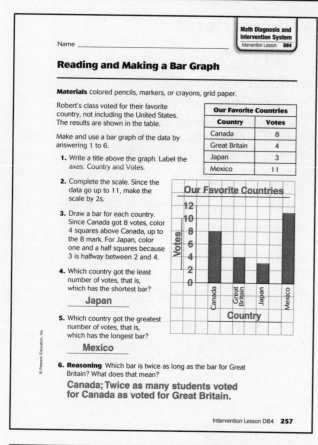

Reading and Making a Bar Graph

Materials colored pencils, markers, or crayons, grid paper.

Robert's class voted for their favorite country, not including the United States. The results are shown in the table.

Make and use a bar graph of the data by answering 1 to 6.

Our Favorite Countries

Country	Votes
Canada	8
Great Britain	4
Japan	3
Mexico	11

1. Write a title above the graph. Label the axes: Country and Votes.

2. Complete the scale. Since the data go up to 11, make the scale by 2s.

3. Draw a bar for each country. Since Canada got 8 votes, color 4 squares above Canada, up to the 8 mark. For Japan, color one and a half squares because 3 is halfway between 2 and 4.

4. Which country got the least number of votes, that is, which has the shortest bar?
   Japan

5. Which country got the greatest number of votes, that is, which has the longest bar?
   Mexico

6. **Reasoning** Which bar is twice as long as the bar for Great Britain? What does that mean?
   Canada; Twice as many students voted for Canada as voted for Great Britain.

© Pearson Education, Inc.

Intervention Lesson D84   **257**

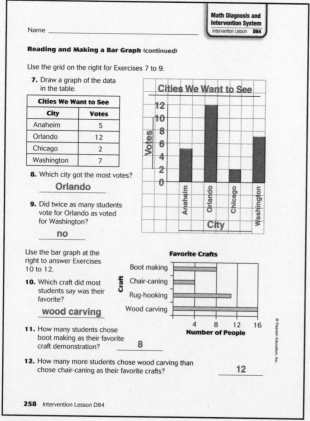

Reading and Making a Bar Graph (continued)

Use the grid on the right for Exercises 7 to 9.

7. Draw a graph of the data in the table.

Cities We Want to See

City	Votes
Anaheim	5
Orlando	12
Chicago	2
Washington	7

8. Which city got the most votes?
   Orlando

9. Did twice as many students vote for Orlando as voted for Washington?
   no

Use the bar graph at the right to answer Exercises 10 to 12.

10. Which craft did most students say was their favorite?
    wood carving

11. How many students chose boot making as their favorite craft demonstration?   **8**

12. How many more students chose wood carving than chose chair-caning as their favorite crafts?   **12**

258   Intervention Lesson D84

Teacher Notes

Ongoing Assessment

If Great Britain had gotten 5 votes, instead of 4, how many grid squares would you color? $2\frac{1}{2}$

Error Intervention

If students do not draw a bar the correct height,

then have them use a ruler or the edge of a piece of paper to compare the height of the bar to the scale. Ask if the place the edge falls on the scale is the same as the number in the table.

If You Have More Time

Have students take a survey of the country or city they would most like to visit and graph the data on grid paper.

Making Line Plots

Name _____

Making Line Plots

A year is sometimes divided into quarters, as show at the right.

1st quarter:	January to March
2nd quarter:	April to June
3rd quarter:	July to September
4th quarter:	October to December

1. Take a survey by asking, "Which quarter of the year were you born?" Write the number of the quarter each person answers in the grid.

Quarter of the Year You Were Born

2. What are all of the possible quarters that can be said?

   1st, 2nd, 3rd, 4th

Answer 3 to 7 to make and use a line plot of the data.

3. Draw a line. Below the line, list in order, all the possible quarters that could be said.   **Line plot data will vary.**

```
 ◄──┼──────┼──────┼──────┼──►
   1st    2nd    3rd    4th
```
Number of Birthdays by Quarter

4. Write "Number of Birthdays by Quarter" below the line plot.

5. For each quarter that was said, mark an X above that quarter on the number line. If more than one X needs to be placed above a quarter, stack them in a single column.   **Answers will vary.**

6. Which quarter has the most number of birthdays? _____

7. How many birthdays are after the 2nd quarter? _____

© Pearson Education, Inc.

Name _____

Making Line Plots (continued)

The nature club leader took a survey of the number of birdfeeders each member had made during camp. The results are shown in the table.

8. Make a line plot to show the data.

Birdfeeders Made During Camp

Member	Made	Member	Made
Ivan	4	Luther	5
Chloe	4	Marco	5
Stacey	3	Victoria	6
Victor	6	Chi	7
Tony	5	Wesley	5
Manny	6	Wendy	5

```
              X
              X
              X      X
       X      X      X
   X   X      X      X
   X   X      X      X      X
 ◄─┼───┼──────┼──────┼──────┼──►
   3   4      5      6      7
```
Number of Birdfeeders Made During Camp

9. How many members made 4 birdfeeders? **2**

10. How many members made 2 birdfeeders? **0**

11. What was the most number of birdfeeders made by a member? **7**

12. How many members made 5 or 6 birdfeeders? **8**

13. How many members made less than 6 birdfeeders? **8**

14. Did more members make more than 5 birdfeeders or less than 5 birdfeeders? **more than 5**

15. **Reasoning** By looking at the line plot, if one more person attended camp, do you think that person would probably make 4 birdfeeders or 5 birdfeeders? Explain.

    Sample answer: The person would probably make 5 birdfeeders, because the most number of people made 5 birdfeeders, and only two people made 4.

© Pearson Education, Inc.

Teacher Notes

Ongoing Assessment

Ask: *By looking at the line plot about the birdfeeders, can you tell how many birdfeeders Chloe made? Explain.* No; a line plot does not show the number each person made.

Error Intervention

If students have trouble reading a complete line plot,

then have the students look at the title below the line plot to see what the Xs represent.

If You Have More Time

Have students take a survey of the number of pets each classmate has. Then make a line plot of the data collected.

How Likely?

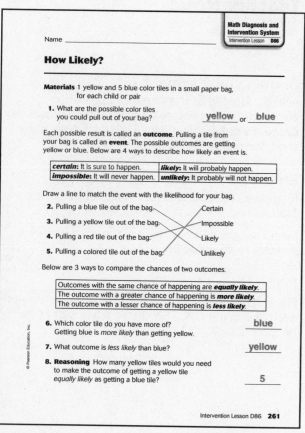

Name _____

How Likely?

Materials 1 yellow and 5 blue color tiles in a small paper bag, for each child or pair

1. What are the possible color tiles you could pull out of your bag?   **yellow** or **blue**

Each possible result is called an **outcome**. Pulling a tile from your bag is called an **event**. The possible outcomes are getting yellow or blue. Below are 4 ways to describe how likely an event is.

certain: It is sure to happen.	**likely:** It will probably happen.
impossible: It will never happen.	**unlikely:** It probably will not happen.

Draw a line to match the event with the likelihood for your bag.

2. Pulling a blue tile out of the bag.   Certain
3. Pulling a yellow tile out of the bag.   Impossible
4. Pulling a red tile out of the bag.   Likely
5. Pulling a colored tile out of the bag.   Unlikely

Below are 3 ways to compare the chances of two outcomes.

Outcomes with the same chance of happening are ***equally likely***.
The outcome with a greater chance of happening is ***more likely***.
The outcome with a lesser chance of happening is ***less likely***.

6. Which color tile do you have more of?   **blue**
Getting blue is *more likely* than getting yellow.

7. What outcome is *less likely* than blue?   **yellow**

8. Reasoning How many yellow tiles would you need to make the outcome of getting a yellow tile *equally likely* as getting a blue tile?   **5**

Intervention Lesson D86   **261**

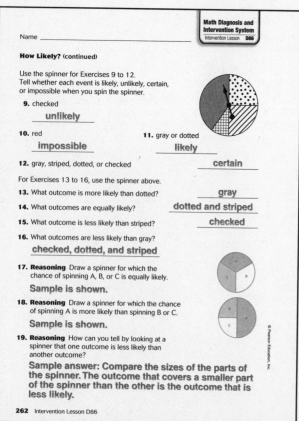

Name _____

How Likely? (continued)

Use the spinner for Exercises 9 to 12.
Tell whether each event is likely, unlikely, certain, or impossible when you spin the spinner.

9. checked   **unlikely**

10. red   **impossible**   **11.** gray or dotted   **likely**

12. gray, striped, dotted, or checked   **certain**

For Exercises 13 to 16, use the spinner above.

13. What outcome is more likely than dotted?   **gray**

14. What outcomes are equally likely?   **dotted and striped**

15. What outcome is less likely than striped?   **checked**

16. What outcomes are less likely than gray?
checked, dotted, and striped

17. Reasoning Draw a spinner for which the chance of spinning A, B, or C is equally likely.
Sample is shown.

18. Reasoning Draw a spinner for which the chance of spinning A is more likely than spinning B or C.
Sample is shown.

19. Reasoning How can you tell by looking at a spinner that one outcome is less likely than another outcome?
Sample answer: Compare the sizes of the parts of the spinner. The outcome that covers a smaller part of the spinner than the other is the outcome that is less likely.

262   Intervention Lesson D86

Teacher Notes

Ongoing Assessment

Ask: ***What is the difference between an impossible event and an unlikely event?*** Sample answer: An impossible event will never happen. There is a good chance that an unlikely event will not happen, but there also is a chance that it will happen.

Error Intervention

If students have trouble with the concept of likely or unlikely,

then use D78: Likely or Unlikely.

If students have trouble with the concept of certain or impossible,

then use D79: Certain or Impossible and D80: Certain, Probable, Impossible.

If You Have More Time

Give each pair of students a bag containing 4 yellow tiles and 1 green tile. Tell them to not look inside the bag. Have them pull a tile out of the bag, record the result in a tally chart, put the tile back in the bag, and repeat at least 10 times. Have them decide which colors are likely, unlikely, impossible, and certain based on the tally chart. Finally, let them look in the bag to check their conclusions.

Outcomes and Experiments

[Student page — top]

Name _____

Outcomes and Experiments

Materials transparent spinner, for each pair or group; red, yellow, blue crayons

A **prediction** tells what may happen using information you know.

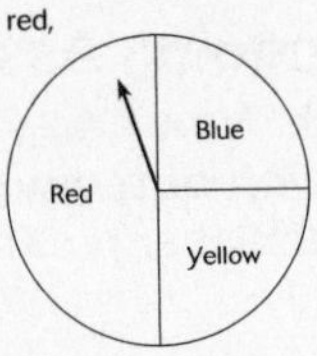

1. Color the spinner at the right.

If you spin the spinner 20 times, how many times would you **predict** spinning each color? Answer 2 to 10 to make and test your predictions.

Spinner: Blue, Red, Yellow

2. How many of the 4 equal parts of the spinner is each color?

___1___ part yellow   ___1___ part blue   ___2___ parts red

So, if you spin the spinner 4 times you would predict that it would land on yellow 1 time, blue 1 time, and red 2 times.

3. Complete the spinning prediction table.

4. How many times do you predict the spinner will land on each color, if you spin the spinner 20 times?

Yellow	1	2	**3**	4	**5**
Blue	1	**2**	3	4	**5**
Red	2	4	**6**	8	**10**
Total Spins	4	8	12	16	20

yellow __5__ times   blue __5__ times   red __10__ times

5. Place the transparent spinner on the spinner above so the centers match. Spin the spinner 20 times. Make a tally chart of your results.

Result	Tally	Number
Yellow		
Blue		
Red		

[Student page — bottom]

Name _____

Outcomes and Experiments (continued)

6. How many times did you spin each color in 20 spins? Results will vary but red should occur about twice as often as yellow or blue.

yellow _____ times   blue _____ times   red _____ times

7. Reasoning How do your predictions compare to your actual spin results? Sample answer: The results were close to the predictions.

8. How many times do you predict the spinner will land on each color, if you spin the spinner 40 times?

yellow __10__ times   blue __10__ times   red __20__ times

9. Spin the spinner 20 more times. Add the results to the tally chart above. How many times did you spin each color in 40 spins? Results will vary but red should occur about twice as often as yellow or blue.

yellow _____ times   blue _____ times   red _____ times
The results should be closer with 40 spins.

10. Reasoning Are your predictions closer to your actual spin results with 20 spins or with 40 spins? _____

11. Complete the table to predict the results of pulling a shape from the bag and returning it, each number of times.

Triangle	7	14	21	28	42	84
Circle	2	**4**	6	**8**	12	**24**
Square	1	2	**3**	**4**	6	12
Total Picks	10	20	**30**	40	60	**120**

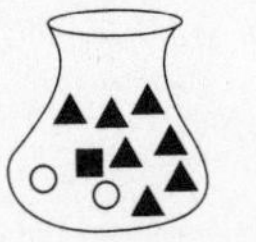

12. Complete the table to predict the results of spinning the spinner, each number of times.

Yellow	3	6	**9**	**12**	**24**	48
Blue	2	**4**	6	8	**16**	32
Total Spins	5	10	15	20	40	**80**

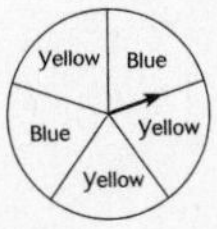

Spinner: Yellow, Blue, Blue, Yellow, Yellow

Teacher Notes

Ongoing Assessment

Ask: *If a spinner is divided into 3 equal parts, and the prediction of spins is 1 blue and 2 red, how is the spinner colored?* One part blue and 2 parts red.

Error Intervention

If students have trouble filling out predictions for the last two columns of the exercises,

then encourage students to write the number of picks that are missing under the total spins in each column.

If You Have More Time

Have partners use 6 color tiles, with variations of their choosing, make a prediction table, and then test their predictions.

Line Plots and Probability

Name _____

Line Plots and Probability

Some answers will vary depending on survey.
Materials 2 cubes, each numbered 1, 1, 2, 2, 3, 3 per pair

1. Toss the two number cubes. Find the sum of the two cubes. Record the sum in a box in the grid. Do this until all 30 boxes are filled.

Sum of Numbers

2. Find, then list all the possible outcomes for the sum of the two number cubes.

$1 + 1 =$ __2__ $1 + 2 =$ __3__

$1 + 3 =$ __4__ $2 + 2 =$ __4__

$2 + 3 =$ __5__ $3 + 3 =$ __6__

__2, 3, 4, 5, 6__

Answer 3 to 7 to make and use a line plot of the results.

Answers will vary, but 4 should have the most X's and 2 and 6 should have the least

3. Draw a line. Below the line, list the possible outcomes in order from least to greatest.

4. Write a title below the line plot.

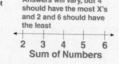

Sum of Numbers

5. For each sum that was rolled, mark an X above that sum on the number line. If more than one X needs to be placed above a sum, stack them in a single column.

6. Which outcome has the most number of Xs? __4__

7. **Reasoning** Predict the next sum most likely to be rolled and least likely to be rolled. Explain.

The sum 4 is most likely because it was tossed the most number of times. The sum 2 or 6 is least likely because it was tossed the least number of times.

© Pearson Education, Inc.

Name _____

Line Plots and Probability (continued)

Larry recorded the total January precipitation (to the nearest inch) for the past 30 years in the chart at the right. Use the data for Exercises 8 to 14.

January Inches of Precipitation					
4	6	3	4	5	4
7	7	5	3	4	5
3	4	5	5	6	7
3	1	4	2	6	5
5	5	5	1	2	1

8. Make a line plot to show the data.

9. How many times did January have 4 inches of precipitation? __6__

10. How many times did January have 5 inches of precipitation? __9__

11. Which number of inches occurred 4 times in the 30 years? __3__

12. Which numbers of inches occurred the same number of times?

__1 inch, 6 inches, and 7 inches__

13. **Reasoning** Why was 0 not included on your line plot?

There were not any times that there were 0 inches of precipitation.

14. **Reasoning** How many inches of precipitation do you predict Larry's area will have next January? Explain.

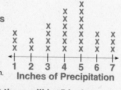

Inches of Precipitation

Sample answer: I predict there will be 5 inches of precipitation because 5 inches of precipitation occurred more often than the other amounts.

© Pearson Education, Inc.

Teacher Notes

Ongoing Assessment

Ask: **How can you use a line plot to predict which outcome(s) is least likely?** The outcome with either no Xs or the least number of Xs is least likely.

Error Intervention

If students have trouble making or reading line plots,

then use D85: Making Line Plots.

If You Have More Time

Have students repeat the activity with the number cubes, however change the labels of one of the cubes to 3, 3, 4, 4, 5, 5. Have the students draw a line plot for the results and predict the next roll.

© Pearson Education, Inc.

Making Bar Graphs to Show Outcomes

Making Bar Graphs to Show Outcomes

Materials 3 index cards (cut in half vertically), bag

1. Write each letter in the word "MUMMY" on an index card. Use the extra index card to make a tally chart for the possible outcomes: M, U, and Y.

2. Place the letters in a bag. Shake them and without looking pick a letter. Tally the letter. Replace the letter, shake, pick, and tally. Do this 20 times.

Answer 3 to 8 to make and use a bar graph of the results.

3. Write the title: Letters Picked from Bag above the graph and label the axes: Outcome and Number of Times.

4. Complete the scale. Make the scale by 2s.

5. Draw a bar for each letter. For every 2 tally marks for the letter M, color in one square above the letter M. After coloring a square for every 2 tallies, if you have a tally left over, color half of a square. Do this for U and Y.

Letters Picked from Bag

(Graph grid with vertical axis labeled "Number of Times" marked 0, 2, 4, 6, 8, 10, 12, 14, 16 and horizontal axis labeled "Outcome" with M, U, Y)

6. Which two letters were picked about the same number of times?
   U and Y

7. Which bar is the longest? **M**
   The lengths of the bars will vary, the bar for M should be the tallest.

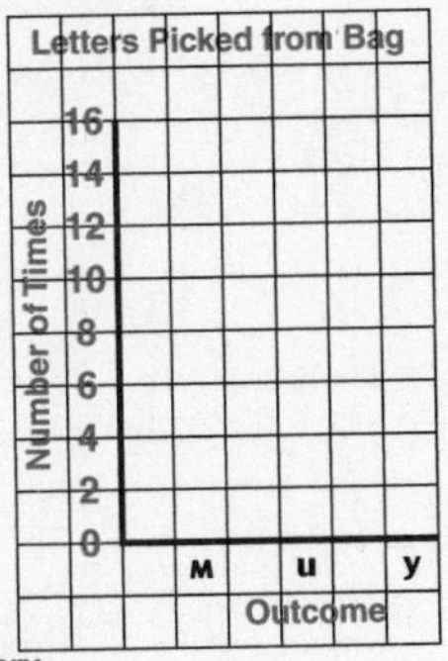

   Since the bar above M is the longest, M is the outcome that occurred most often.

8. **Reasoning** Predict the next letter picked. Explain how you made your prediction.
   M; it is the outcome that occurred most often.

Intervention Lesson D89 **267**

© Pearson Education, Inc.

Making Bar Graphs to Show Outcomes (continued)

Kendra spun a spinner 20 times. She recorded the number of times each color was spun. Use the data for Exercises 9 to 13.

Spinner Results

Outcome	Tally	Number
Purple	|||| ||||		11
Green	||||	4
Orange	||||	4
Yellow			1

9. Make a bar graph in the grid on the right to show the data.

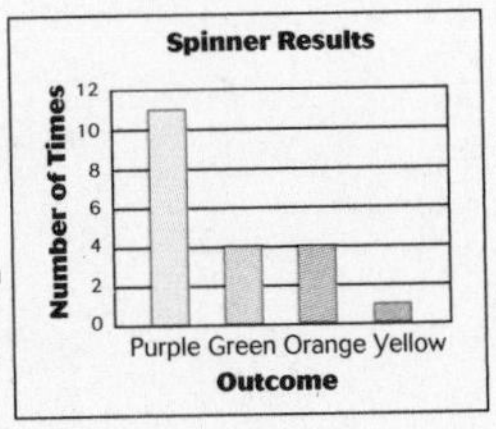

10. Which color occurred most often? least often?
    purple; yellow

11. **Reasoning** What can you tell from the orange and green bars?
    Sample answer: Orange and green were spun the same number of times.

12. **Reasoning** Which color do you predict would be spun next?
    purple

13. **Reasoning** Draw what you think the spinner looked like that Kendra used.
    Sample spinner is shown.

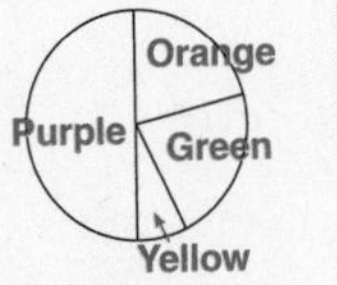

Spinner Results

(Bar graph with vertical axis "Number of Times" marked 0, 2, 4, 6, 8, 10, 12 and horizontal axis "Outcome" with Purple, Green, Orange, Yellow)

(Pie chart spinner showing Orange, Purple, Green, Yellow)

© Pearson Education, Inc.

268 Intervention Lesson D89

© Pearson Education, Inc.

Teacher Notes

Ongoing Assessment

Ask: *How can you tell which color on a spinner covers the most area by looking at a bar graph?* The color that has the longest bar probably has the largest area on the spinner.

Error Intervention

If students have trouble make or reading bar graphs,

then use D84: Reading and Making a Bar Graph, D71: Reading Bar Graphs, and D75: Making Bar Graphs.

If You Have More Time

Have students repeat the activity, but with the word "COMPUTER". Pick one letter from the bag 40 times. After the students have drawn their bar graph, ask: *Will it be easy to predict what letter would be drawn next?* Sample answer: No, all the letters were drawn about the same amount of times. It could be any of the letters. Then ask: *Why do you think all the letters were drawn about the same number of times?* There are only 1 of each letter. So they are all equally likely to be drawn.

Name _____

Time

1.

2.

_____   _____   _____

- - - - - - - - - - -   - - - - - - - - - - -   - - - - - - - - - - -

_____   _____   _____

3.

1. Ask: *What is the boy doing in the first picture?* He is putting on his socks. *What are the people doing in the second picture?* They are watching a movie. *Which takes more time?* Watching a movie takes more time. Have children circle the activity that takes more time.

2. Have children look at the zoo pictures. Have children put a 1 under the picture that shows what happens first, a 2 under the picture that shows what happens next, and a 3 under the picture which shows what happens last.

3. Ask children what is happening in each picture and if it is morning, afternoon, or evening.

Name _____

Time (continued)

Circle the activity in each exercise that takes more time.

4.

5.

Write 1, 2, and 3, to order the events.

6.

_____   _____   _____

------------   ------------   ------------

_____   _____   _____

Name _____

Days and Seasons

1.

2.

3.

4.

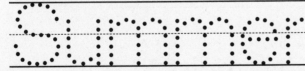

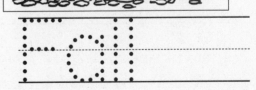

Materials: Crayons or markers

1. Say: ***The first picture shows winter, as it looks in the north. What is winter like?*** Have children describe winter as snowy and cold. The trees don't have leaves. Have children trace the word Winter and color the picture. The tree should be brown and the snow should be left white.

2. Say: ***The next picture shows spring. What is spring like?*** Have children describe spring. Have children trace the word Spring and color the picture. The tree should be brown with light green leaves, the pond should be blue, and the hills should be light green.

3. Repeat with summer and fall. Summer: The leaves of the tree should be a darker green than in spring, the pond should be blue, and the hills should be green. Fall: The tree should be brown with brown, orange, and red leaves, the pond should be blue, and the hills should be green.

Name ______________________________

Days and Seasons (continued)

Write the name of each day.
Draw a line from the day to a number to show the order.

Tuesday	1
Monday	2
Friday	3
Sunday	4
Saturday	5
Wednesday	6
Thursday	7

Math Diagnosis and
Intervention System
Intervention Lesson   D3

Calendar

March

Sunday	Monday	Tuesday	Wednesday	Thursday	Friday	Saturday
				1	2	3
4	5			8		
11			14		16	
	19	20			23	24
25			28	29	30	31

April

Sunday	Monday	Tuesday	Wednesday	Thursday	Friday	Saturday
1	2		4			
	9		11	12		14

Materials: Crayons or markers

1. Have children trace and write the missing numbers on the calendars.
2. Have children circle Friday and all the dates in that column with red.
3. Have children circle Tuesday and all the dates in that column with blue.
4. Have children put an X through March 8, 11, 24, 28, and April 9.

© Pearson Education, Inc.

Calendar (continued)

1. Write the numbers in the calendar.

2. Circle Thursday and all the dates in that column.

3. Circle Monday and all the dates in that column.

4. Put an X on December 6, 12, 22, and 30.

December						
Sunday	Monday	Tuesday	Wednesday	Thursday	Friday	Saturday
			2	3		
	7					12
13					18	
		22				
		30	31			

Time to the Hour

1.

2. _____ o'clock

3.

   _____ o'clock

4.

   _____ o'clock

5. _____ o'clock

6. 6 o'clock

7. 3 o'clock

Materials: Crayons or markers

1. Say: *A clock has at least two hands. The longer hand is the minute hand.* Have children color the minute hand blue. *The shorter hand is the hour hand.* Have children color the hour hand red.

2. Have children circle the numbers on the clock as the class reads them out loud, together, starting with 1.

3. Say: *At 7 o'clock, the hour hand is on the 7 and the minute hand is on the 12. The big clock shows 7 o'clock.* Have children write 7 in the blank next to the clock.

4. Have children write the time for each of the clocks in 3–5.

5. Have children draw the minute hand to show 6 o'clock and the hour hand to show 3 o'clock.

Time to the Hour (continued)

Color the hour hand  ~~red~~.
Circle the number to which it points.
Write the time.

8.

_____ o'clock

9.

_____ o'clock

10.

_____ o'clock

11.

_____ o'clock

12.

_____ o'clock

13.

_____ o'clock

Time to the Half Hour

1.

$8{:}00$

_____ o'clock

2.

$4{:}30$

half past _____ 4

3.

___ : ___

_____ o'clock

4.

___ : ___

half past _____

Materials: Crayons or markers

1. Say: *A clock has at least two hands. The longer hand is the minute hand.* Have children color the minute hand blue. *The shorter hand is the hour hand.* Have children color the hour hand red.

2. Have children circle the numbers the minute and hour hands are pointing to in number 1. Say: *The clock shows 8 o'clock.* Have children write 8:00 and 8.

3. Have children circle the number the minute hand is pointing to in number 2. Say: *When the minute hand is on the 6, it is half past the hour. A half hour is 30 minutes. The clock shows half past 4 or four thirty.* Have children write 4:30 and 4.

4. Have children write the other times similarly.

Time to the Half Hour (continued)

Write each time.

5.

7:30
____

Half past ___7___

6.

____:____

Half past _____

7.

____:____

_____ o'clock

8.

____:____

Half past _____

9.

____:____

Half past _____

10.

____:____

Half past _____

11.

____:____

Half past _____

12.

____:____

_____ o'clock

13.

____:____

Half past _____

Ordering and Estimating Time

I. A

about I minute

- - - - - - about I hour

about I day

2. B

about I minute

about I hour

about I day

3. C

about I minute

about I hour

about I day

4. _____ _____ _____
shortest   longest

---

1. Ask children to name things they do which take about a minute. Say: ***It takes about a minute to . . .*** Then rename the best examples. Repeat the exercise for *hour* and *day*. If necessary, give examples such as, from the time we start math until we finish recess is one hour.

2. Ask children to describe the first picture. Ask: ***Does a soccer game take about 1 minute, about 1 hour, or about 1 day?*** Have children draw a line from the picture to "about 1 hour."

3. Ask children to describe the second picture. Ask: ***How long does it take to brush your teeth—about 1 minute, about 1 hour, or about 1 day?*** Have children draw a line from the picture to "about 1 minute."

4. Ask a similar question for the last picture.

5. Ask: ***Which takes the shortest amount of time, playing soccer, brushing your teeth, or painting a room?*** Have children write B in the blank above shortest since there is a B by brushing your teeth. Find which activity takes the longest time, and which is in the middle, similarly.

Ordering and Estimating Time (continued)

About how long does each activity take?
Draw lines to match.

5.

2 minutes

2 hours

2 days

6.

1 minute

1 hour

1 day

7.

1 minute

1 hour

1 day

8.

1 minute

1 hour

1 day

9.

1 minute

1 hour

1 day

10.

3 minutes

3 hours

3 days

11. Reasoning Draw something you like to do that takes all day.

Math Diagnosis and
Intervention System
Intervention Lesson   D7

Using a Calendar

January

S	M	T	W	T	F	S
	1	2	3	4	5	6
7	8	9	10	11	12	13
14	15	16	17	18	19	20
21	22	23	24	25	26	27
28	29	30	31			

February

S	M	T	W	T	F	S
				1	2	3
4	5	6	7	8	9	10
11	12	13	14	15	16	17
18	19	20	21	22	23	24
25	26	27	28			

March

S	M	T	W	T	F	S
				1	2	3
4	5	6	7	8	9	10
11	12	13	14	15	16	17
18	19	20	21	22	23	24
25	26	27	28	29	30	31

April

S	M	T	W	T	F	S
1	2	3	4	5	6	7
8	9	10	11	12	13	14
15	16	17	18	19	20	21
22	23	24	25	26	27	28
29	30					

May

S	M	T	W	T	F	S
		1	2	3	4	5
6	7	8	9	10	11	12
13	14	15	16	17	18	19
20	21	22	23	24	25	26
27	28	29	30	31		

June

S	M	T	W	T	F	S
					1	2
3	4	5	6	7	8	9
10	11	12	13	14	15	16
17	18	19	20	21	22	23
24	25	26	27	28	29	30

July

S	M	T	W	T	F	S
1	2	3	4	5	6	7
8	9	10	11	12	13	14
15	16	17	18	19	20	21
22	23	24	25	26	27	28
29	30	31				

August

S	M	T	W	T	F	S
			1	2	3	4
5	6	7	8	9	10	11
12	13	14	15	16	17	18
19	20	21	22	23	24	25
26	27	28	29	30	31	

September

S	M	T	W	T	F	S
						1
2	3	4	5	6	7	8
9	10	11	12	13	14	15
16	17	18	19	20	21	22
23	24	25	26	27	28	29
30						

October

S	M	T	W	T	F	S
	1	2	3	4	5	6
7	8	9	10	11	12	13
14	15	16	17	18	19	20
21	22	23	24	25	26	27
28	29	30	31			

November

S	M	T	W	T	F	S
				1	2	3
4	5	6	7	8	9	10
11	12	13	14	15	16	17
18	19	20	21	22	23	24
25	26	27	28	29	30	

December

S	M	T	W	T	F	S
						1
2	3	4	5	6	7	8
9	10	11	12	13	14	15
16	17	18	19	20	21	22
23	24	25	26	27	28	29
30	31					

1. __12__   2. __August__

1. Say: *Each page in a calendar shows a month. This calendar shows a year. How many months are in a year?* Have children write 12.

2. Say the names of the months together as a class. Ask: *What month comes after July?* Have children write August. Say: *Find March 9th on the calendar. Circle it.*

Using a Calendar (continued)

Use the calendar below.

April						
Sunday	**Monday**	**Tuesday**	**Wednesday**	**Thursday**	**Friday**	**Saturday**
			1	2		
				30		

3. Write the numbers in the calendar.

....

4. Color the first day of the month RED.

....

5. Color all the Mondays YELLOW.

....

6. Find the date one week after the 14th.
Color that date BLUE.

....

7. What is the date one week after April 15? _____

© Pearson Education, Inc.

Time to Five Minutes

1. 5, <u>10</u>, ____, ____, ____, ____, 35, ____, ____, ____, ____, 60

2.

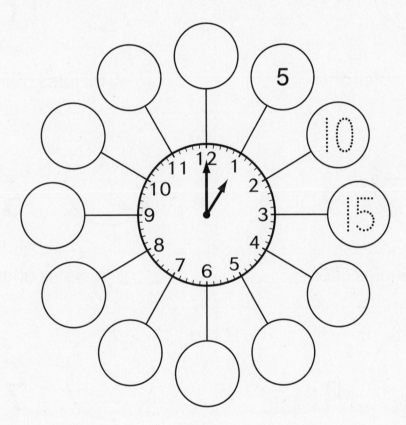

3.  <u>5</u> minutes after <u>8</u>   8:05

---

1. Have children skip count by fives and write the missing numbers.
2. Say: *It takes the minute hand 5 minutes to move from one number to the next on a clock. When the minute hand is on the 1, it is 5 minutes after the hour. When the minute hand is on the 2, it is 10 minutes after the hour.* Have children count by fives around the clock and write the numbers.
3. Ask: *What number did you write by the 8?* 40 *When the minute hand is on the 8, it is 40 after the hour.*
4. Ask: *What is the hour shown on the clock in number 3?* 8 *How many minutes is it after 8?* Have children complete 5 minutes after 8. Say: *Write 5 minutes after 8 like this.* Write 8:05 on the board or overhead and have children write to complete it on paper.

Name _____

Time to Five Minutes (continued)

Find the minutes after the hour. Write the time in two ways.

4.    9:35

35 minutes after 9

5.    11:50

50 minutes after 11

6.    9:___

_____ minutes after _____

7.    6:___

_____ minutes after _____

8.    4:___

_____ minutes after _____

9.    7:___

_____ minutes after _____

10.    8:___

_____ minutes after _____

11.    3:___

_____ minutes after _____

Name _____

Time Before and After the Hour

I.

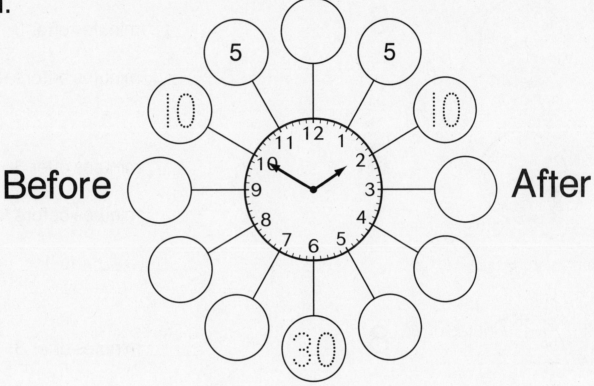

2. 1: ____   10 minutes before 2

3.    ____ minutes after 2

2: ____   half past 2

Materials: Crayons or Markers

1. Have children count by fives and fill in the circles up to 30. Then have them count by fives again and fill in the circles starting with 5 by the 11 on the clock, 10 by the 10, 15 by the 9 and so on. Explain that these numbers show how many minutes it is before the hour.

2. Ask: *What time is shown on the clock?* One fifty or fifty after one; Have children write 50. *When it is one fifty, how long is it until it is 2:00?* 10 minutes *Another way to say the time when it is one fifty or fifty after one is ten to two or ten minutes before two.* Have children trace 10.

3. Ask: *What time does the clock in item 3 show?* Have children write 30 twice. Say: *Another way to say two thirty or thirty after two is half past two.* Have children trace half past.

Math Diagnosis and
Intervention System
Intervention Lesson   **D9**

Time Before and After the Hour (continued)

Write the time more than one way.

4.

3:____

____ minutes after 3

____ minutes before 4

5.

3:____

____ minutes after 3

____ minutes before 4

_____ to 4

6.

8:____

____ minutes after 8

_____ 8

7.

5:____

____ minutes after 5

_____ after 5

Reasoning Draw the hands on the clock to show the time.

8.

It is quarter to 12.

9.

It is half past 6.

Name _____

Equivalent Times

1.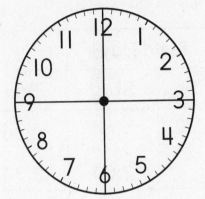

2.

Equivalent Times	
One quarter hour	15 minutes
One half hour	_____ minutes
One hour	_____ minutes

3.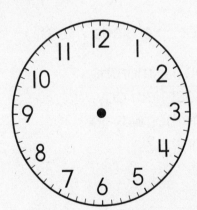

Materials: Crayons or Markers

1. Have children color one fourth of the clock between the 12 and the 3. Say: *It takes the minute hand one fourth of an hour to move from 12 to 3.* Have children draw hands on the second clock to show quarter after 12. Ask: *Quarter after 12 is how many minutes after 12?* 15 *How many minutes equal one quarter hour?* Have children write 15 in the table. Say: *One quarter hour and 15 minutes are equivalent times.*

2. Have children color the one half of the clock between 12 and 6. Say: *It takes the minute hand one half of an hour to move from 12 to 6.* Have children draw hands to show half past 12. Ask: *Half past 12 is how many minutes after 12?* 30 *How many minutes equal one half hour?* 30 Have children write 30 in the table. Say: *One half hour and 30 minutes are equivalent times.*

3. Ask: *How many minutes are in an hour?* Have children skip count by 5s all the way around the clock and write 60 in the table.

Equivalent Times (continued)

Use the schedule for Exercises 4 to 6.
Write 2 ways to say how long each event lasts.

4. Relay Race

_____

_____

Field Day		
Event	Start	End
Parade	1:00	2:00
Relay Race	2:00	2:30
100 yd Dash	2:30	2:45

5. Parade   _____   _____

6. 100-Yard Dash   _____   _____

Use the table for Exercises 7 to 8.

7. It has been 12 months
since the last field day.
What is another way to
say 12 months?

_____

8. It took 1 week to plan field day.
What is another way to say 1 week?   _____

Equivalent Times	
1 day	24 hours
1 week	7 days
1 year	12 months

9. Reasoning
How many days are equal to 2 weeks?   _____

Name _____

Comparing Temperatures

I.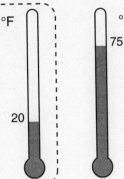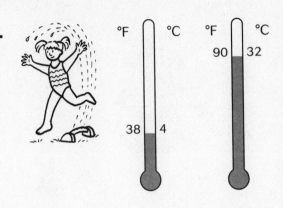

2.

3.

4.

---

1. Ask: *Do people go sled riding when it is hot outside or when it is cold outside?* cold
   Say: *Temperature is measured with a thermometer. A Thermometer shows a low temperature when it is cold.* Have children circle the thermometer with a low temperature.

2. Ask: *Do people play in a water sprinkler when the weather is hot or when it is cold?* hot
   Say: *A thermometer shows a high temperature when it is hot.* Have children circle the thermometer with a high temperature.

3. Say: *The first picture shows a bowl of cereal.* Ask: *Which bowl has something hotter?* Have children circle the bowl of hot soup.

4. Have children circle the picture which shows something colder than the inside of a gym.

Comparing Temperatures (continued)

Circle hot or cold.

5.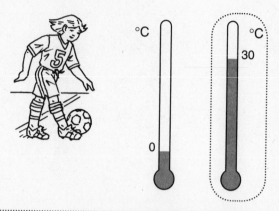

6.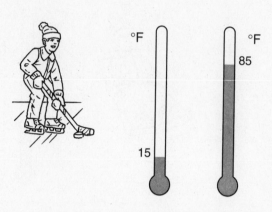

7. Circle what is hotter than:

      or

8. Circle what is colder than:

      or

9. Circle what is the same temperature as:

      or

Name _____

Measuring Temperature

I.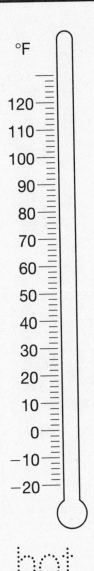

2.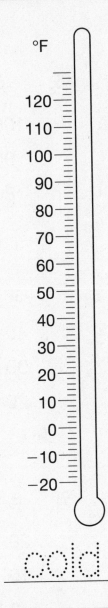

3.

hot   cold

© Pearson Education, Inc.

Materials: Crayons or Markers

1. Say: *Temperature tells how hot or cold something is. One way to measure temperature is in degrees Fahrenheit, using a thermometer.* Write 80°F on the board and explain how to read it. Have children find 80 on the thermometer and then color it from the circle at the bottom up to 80.

2. Say: *Now your thermometer shows 80 degrees Fahrenheit. Is it hot or cold outside when it is 80 degrees?* hot; Have children trace the word hot. Have children name activities they do when it is 80 degrees outside.

3. Have children color in the second thermometer to show 30 degrees. Ask: *Is it hot or cold outside when it is 30 degrees Fahrenheit?* cold; Have children trace the word cold. Have children name activities they do when it is 30 degrees outside.

4. Have children color the third thermometer to show 65 degrees. Help them count by 2s for the tick marks and color up to a line between the tick marks for 64 and 66. Discuss that the weather is warm, not hot at 65°.

Measuring Temperature (continued)

Write each temperature.
Then circle hot or cold.

4.
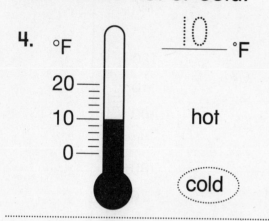
_____10_____ °F

hot

(cold)

5.
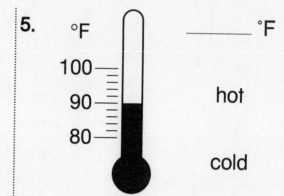
_____ °F

hot

cold

6.
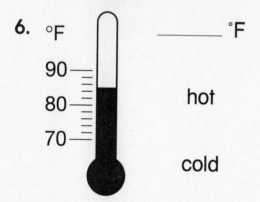
_____ °F

hot

cold

7.
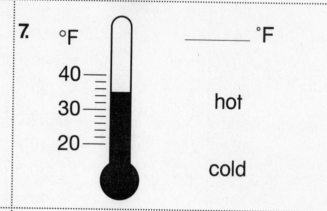
_____ °F

hot

cold

8.
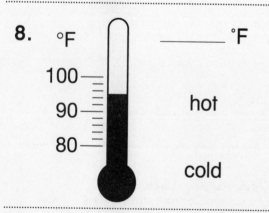
_____ °F

hot

cold

9.
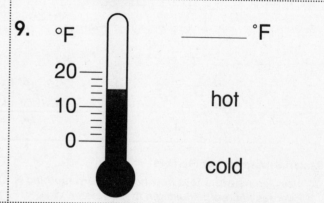
_____ °F

hot

cold

10. Reasoning Circle the thermometer that shows the coldest temperature.

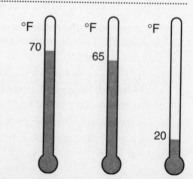

Name _____

Time to the Quarter Hour

Use the clocks at the right to answer 1 to 6.

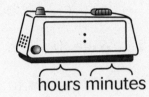

1. What two numbers is the hour hand between?

_____ and _____

2. Since the hour hand has not reached the 1, it is after
12:00. Write 12 for the hours in the digital clock.

hours   minutes

3. What number is the minute hand on?   _____

4. Each number on the clock represents
5 minutes after the hour. Count by 5s.
How many minutes is it after 12?   _____

5. Write 15 for the minutes in the digital clock.

The clock shows 12:15 or twelve fifteen.

6. Write 12:15 in two other ways.

15 minutes past _____;   quarter past _____

Use the clock at the right to answer 7 to 11.

7. What two numbers is the hour hand between?

_____ and _____

8. What is the hour? _____

9. What number is the minute hand on?   _____

10. Count by 5s. How many minutes is it after the hour?   _____

11. Write the time in three ways.

_____ : _____;   _____ minutes past _____;   _____ past _____

Name _____

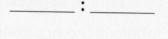

Time to the Quarter Hour (continued)

For Exercises 12 to 15, use the clock at the right.

12. What time is shown on the clock?   _____ : _____

13. What hour is it about to be?   _____

14. Count by 5s. How many minutes is it before 2 o'clock?   _____

15. Write the time in two other ways.

15 minutes to _____;   quarter to _____

Write the hour and then the minutes after the hour. Then circle the two correct times.

16.

hour _____

minutes _____

2:45   3:45   1:45

quarter   15 minutes   quarter
to 2   to 3   past 2

17.

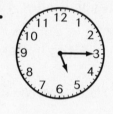

hour _____

minutes _____

4:15   6:15   5:15

quarter   quarter   15 minutes
past 6   past 5   to 5

18.

hour _____

minutes _____

7:30   8:30   9:30

half   quarter   30 minutes
past 8   past 8   past 9

19.

hour _____

minutes _____

11:45   11:15   12:45

quarter   15 minutes   quarter
to 11   to 11   to 12

Telling Time

Find the time on the clock by answering 1 to 8.

1. What two numbers is the hour hand between?

_____ and _____

2. Since the hour hand has not reached the 6, it is after 5:00. Write 5 for the hours in the digital clock.

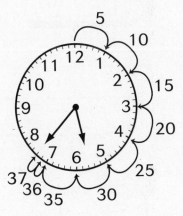

hours minutes

3. It takes the minute hand 5 minutes to move from one number to the next. To find the minutes, first count by 5s from the 12 to the 7. Then count by 1s for each small mark after the 7.

4. How many minutes is it after 5? _____
Write the minutes in the digital clock above.

5. Write the time in three different ways.

_____ : _____;

_____ thirty-seven;

_____ minutes past 5

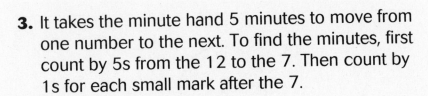

6. To find how many minutes before the next hour, count the other way. Count by 5s from the 12 to the 8, then count by 1s for each small mark after the 8.

7. How many minutes is it before 6? _____

8. Write the time another way.

_____ minutes to 6

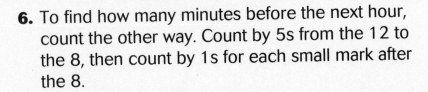

9. Write the time shown on the clock at the right in two different ways.

_____ twenty-_____; _____ minutes past 2

2 : 24

Name _____

Telling Time (continued)

Write the time shown on each clock in two ways.

10.

_____

_____

11.

_____

_____

12.

_____

_____

13.

_____

_____

14.

_____

_____

15.

_____

_____

16. Reasoning When finding the number of minutes on the clock at the right, why do you first count by 5s and then by ones?

Units of Time

Benny spent 3 weeks at his cousin's house. Find how many days
Benny spent at his cousin's by using the table and answering
1 to 3.

1. 1 week = _____ days

Relating Units of Time		
1 week	=	7 days
1 day	=	24 hours
1 hour	=	60 minutes

2. To find how many days are in 3 weeks,
multiply 3 × 7 days.

   3 × 7 days = _____ days

3. How many days did Benny spend at his cousin's? _____ days

The talent show lasted 2 hours and 17 minutes. Find how many
minutes the talent show lasted by using the table and answering
4 to 6.

4. 1 hour = _____ minutes

5. First, find the number of minutes in 2 hours. Then add the
17 minutes.

   2 × 60 minutes = _____ minutes

   120 minutes + 17 minutes = _____ minutes

6. How many minutes did the talent show last? _____ minutes

Cindy left her radio on for 4 days, 5 hours. Find how many hours
Cindy's radio stayed on by using the table and answering 7 to 9.

7. 1 day = _____ hours

8. First find the number of hours in 4 days. Then add the 5 hours.

   4 × 24 hours = _____ hours

   96 hours + 5 hours = _____ hours

9. How many hours did Cindy's radio stay on? _____ hours

Units of Time (continued)

Find the missing numbers.

10. 6 hours = _____ minutes   **11.** 8 days = _____ hours

12. 9 weeks = _____ days   **13.** 5 hours = _____ minutes

14. 5 days, 3 hours = _____ hours   **15.** 1 hour, 2 minutes = _____ minutes

16. 6 weeks, 6 days = _____ days   **17.** 3 days, 16 hours = _____ hours

18. The first space flight when humans orbited the earth lasted
1 hour, 48 minutes.
How many minutes did the flight last?   _____

19. The first space flight when humans orbited the moon
lasted 6 days, 3 hours. How many hours did the
mission last?   _____

20. It normally takes a duck egg 4 weeks, 2 days to
hatch. How many days is 4 weeks, 2 days?   _____

21. It normally takes a pigeon egg 2 weeks, 4 days to
hatch. How many days is 2 weeks, 4 days?   _____

22. Reasoning A chicken egg normally hatches in 21 days.
A turkey egg normally hatches in 3 weeks, 5 days. How
many more days does it normally take a turkey egg to
hatch than a chicken egg? Explain how you solved.

23. Eddie ran a marathon in 4 hours and 7 minutes. His goal
was to finish the race in less than 250 minutes. Did Eddie
achieve his goal? Explain your reasoning.

Elapsed Time

The party starts at 2:00 P.M. and ends at 4:45 P.M. How long is the party?

Start     **End**

1. How many hours from 2:00 P.M. to 4:00 P.M.?   _____ hours

2. How many minutes from 4:00 P.M. to 4:45 P.M.?   _____ minutes

3. How long did the party last?   _____ hours, _____ minutes

School starts at 8:20 A.M. and ends at 3:30 P.M. How long does school last?

Start     **End**

4. How many hours from 8:20 A.M. to 3:20 P.M.?   _____ hours

5. How many minutes from 3:20 P.M. to 3:30 P.M.?   _____ minutes

6. How long does school last?   _____ hours, _____ minutes

Reasoning The flight lasted 3 hours 20 minutes. If the plane took off at 4:10 P.M., what time did it land?

7. What time is 3 hours after 4:10 P.M.?   _____ P.M.

8. What time is 20 minutes after 7:10 P.M.   _____ P.M.

9. What time did the plane land?   _____ P.M.

Elapsed Time (continued)

Find the elapsed time.

10. Start Time: 1:00 P.M.
End Time: 8:00 P.M.

_____

11. Start Time: 7:00 A.M.
End Time: 10:35 A.M.

_____

12. Start Time: 11:35 A.M.
End Time: 3:50 P.M.

_____

13. Start Time: 6:10 P.M.
End Time: 12:25 A.M.

_____

14. Start Time: 2:00 P.M.
End Time: 6:05 P.M.

_____

15. Start Time: 9:20 A.M.
End Time: 2:40 P.M.

_____

16. Start Time: 4:35 P.M.
End Time: 5:15 P.M.

_____

17. Start Time: 8:15 A.M.
End Time: 2:55 A.M.

_____

18. Reasoning The baseball game started at
3:00 P.M. It lasted 2 hours and 45 minutes.
What time did the baseball game end?

_____

19. Reasoning Erin got home from the
soccer match at 5:20 P.M. She went to
bed 3 hours and 45 minutes later.
What time did she go to bed?

_____

20. Reasoning The rainstorm began at
1:15 P.M. Marco's class came in from
recess 25 minutes earlier. What time
did the class come in from recess?

_____

21. Reasoning What is 30 minutes before
12:25 P.M.?

_____

Temperature

Temperature is the measure of how hot or how cold something is.

Temperature can be measured in **degrees Fahrenheit** (°F) or **degrees Celsius** (°C).

1. Look at the thermometer at the right. Does the right side show °F or °C?   _____

2. What is the temperature in °C?   _____

Find the temperature in °F by answering 3 to 7.

3. Which side shows °F?   _____

4. Look at the left side of the thermometer. How many spaces are between 30° and 40°?   _____

5. What is 40° − 30°?   _____

6. Each space on the left side of the thermometer equals how many degrees? 10° ÷ 5 = _____

7. Start at 60°F. Then count up by 2s to where the dark bar stops.

60, 62, _____, _____, _____

The top of the dark bar is at 68, so the temperature is 68°F.

8. Reasoning Would you build a snowman in 34°F or 64°F weather? Use the table to decide and explain your reasoning.

	°F	°C
Water boils	212	100
Normal body temperature	98.6	37
Room temperature	68	20
Water Freezes	32	0

Temperature (continued)

Choose the better temperature for each activity.

9. bicycle riding   **10.** camping   **11.** ice skating   **12.** wearing shorts

30°F or 70°F   0°C or 30°C   32°F or 72°F   35°C or 100°C

Choose the better estimate for the temperature.

13. hot pizza   **14.** ice cream   **15.** bathwater   **16.** cold drink

80°F or 160°F   0°C or 30°C   45°F or 95°F   0°C or 10°C

Write each temperature in °F and °C.

17.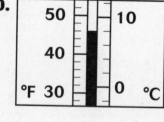

_____°F   _____°C

18.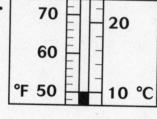

_____°F   _____°C

19.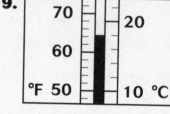

_____°F   _____°C

20.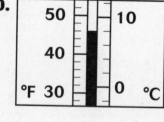

_____°F   _____°C

21.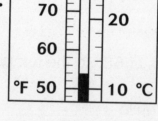

_____°F   _____°C

22.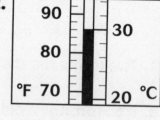

_____°F   _____°C

23. One cold morning, the temperature was 35°F. The
temperature rose to 53°F later in the day. How many
degrees had the temperature increased?

_____

24. Reasoning This morning the temperature was 65°F.
Then it rose 3°. Then the temperature dropped 10°.
What was the final temperature?

_____

Name _____

Comparing and Ordering by Length

1.

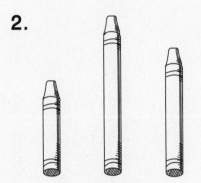

2.

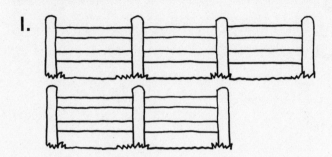

3. Reasoning

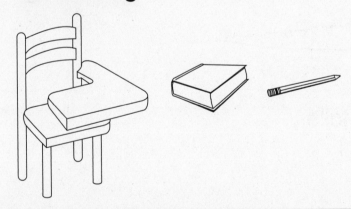

Materials: Snap cubes, crayons or markers

1. Ask: **Which fence is longer?** Have children color the longer fence.

2. Ask: **Which crayon is the tallest?** Have children color the tallest crayon red. **Which crayon is the shortest?** Have children color the shortest crayon blue.

3. Have children put together snap cubes to make a train the same length as a book. Then have them use the train to compare the length of the book to the length of their desks. Ask: **Which is longer, the book or the desk?** The desk should be longer. Then have them use the train to compare the length of the book to the length of a pencil. Ask: **Which is shorter the book or the pencil?** The pencil should be shorter.

4. Ask: **Which is the longest, the desk, the pencil, or the book?** Have children circle the desk. Ask: **Which is the shortest, the desk, the pencil, or the book?** Have children put an X on the pencil.

Comparing and Ordering by Length (continued)

Color the longest .

Color the shortest [BLUE crayon].

4.

5.

6. Color the one that is taller.

Name _____

Comparing and Ordering by Capacity

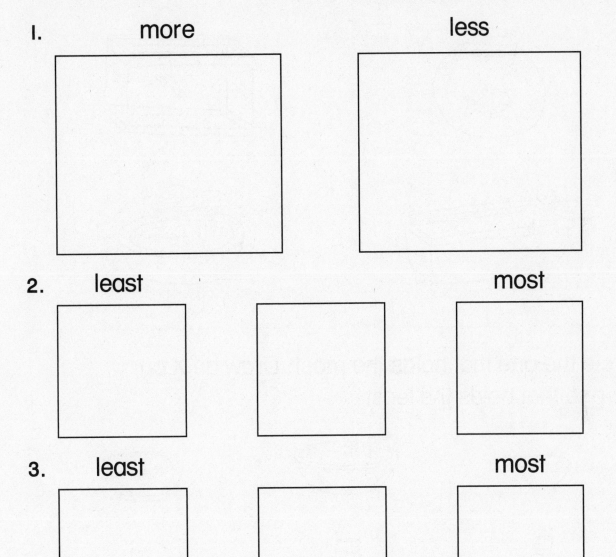

1. more   less

2. least   most

3. least   most

Materials: Rice, various size containers—one set of 3 for each pair or group

1. Have children choose two containers. Have them fill one of the two with rice. Then, have them try to fill the second container with the rice from the first container. Ask: **Which container holds more rice?** Have children draw a picture of the container that holds more in the first box. Ask: **Which container holds less?** Have children draw a picture of the container that holds less in the second box.

2. Have children use the rice to decide which of their 3 containers holds the least and draw a picture of it in the first box. Have them decide which holds the most and draw a picture in the last box. Then have them draw a picture of the other container in the middle.

3. Have children trade containers with another pair or group and order the containers by capacity the same way.

Comparing and Ordering by Capacity (continued)

Circle the one that holds more.

4.

 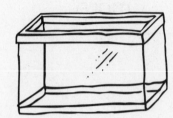

5.

Circle the one that holds the most. Draw an X on the one that holds the least.

6.

7.

8.

Comparing and Ordering by Weight

1.   heavier   lighter

2.   heaviest   lightest

3.   heaviest   lightest

Materials: Various objects of obviously different weights, one set of 3 for each pair or group.

1.   Have children choose two of the objects. Have each child hold the objects, one in each hand to decide which is heavier and which is lighter. Have children draw a picture of the object which is heavier in the first box and the one which is lighter in the second box.

2.   Have children decide which of their three objects is the heaviest and draw a picutre in the first box. Have them decide which is the lightest and draw a picture in the last box. Have them draw a picture of the other object in the middle box.

3.   Have children trade objects with another pair or group and order the objects by weight, the same way.

Comparing and Ordering by Weight (continued)

Color the heavier object  .

Color the lighter object  .

4.

5.

6.

7.

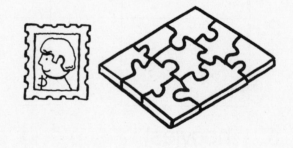

8. Color the heaviest object  .

Color the lightest object  .

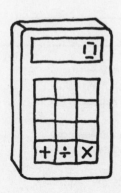

Comparing Areas

I.

7

2.

_____

Materials: Color tiles or cut-out squares that are 1-inch on a side—9 for each child, crayons or markers

1. Have children put color tiles on the figure to cover it. Ask: *How many tiles did it take to cover the figure?* Have children write 7. Say: *The area of the figure is 7 squares.*

2. Have children find and write the area of the second figure. Ask: *Which figure covers more area?* Have children color the second figure since it covers more area.

Comparing Areas (continued)

Write how many tiles it takes to cover each.
Color the one that covers more area.

3.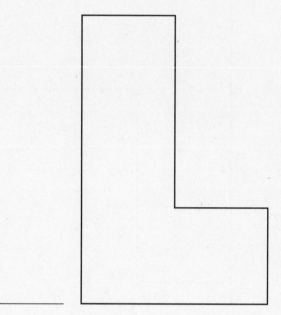

_____   _____

4.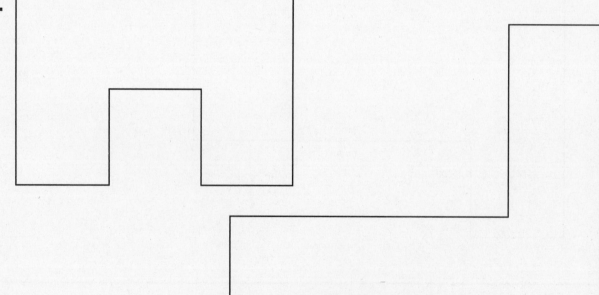

_____   _____

Name _____

Unit Size and Measuring

1.

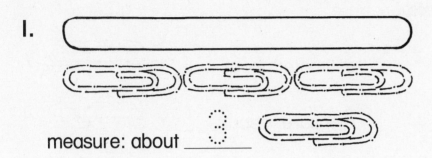

measure: about _____

2.

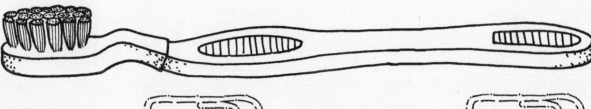

estimate: about _____   measure: about _____

3.

estimate: about _____   measure: about _____

4. Estimate: about _____   Measure: about _____

5. Estimate: about _____   Measure: about _____

Materials: Snap cubes, 20 for each child; paper clips, 10 for each child

1. Say: *In order to measure, you compare a unit, like the length of a paper clip, to the length of an object. How many paper clips long is the craft stick?* Have children write 3. *Notice how the paper clips are lined up straight with no spaces between. This is important.*

2. Ask: *How many paper clips long do you think the toothbrush is? Write your guess or estimate.* Have children measure the length of the toothbrush by lining up paperclips and write 5. Compare the estimates to the measures.

3. Estimate and measure the pencil similarly.

4. Ask: *How many snap cubes long do you think the toothbrush is?* Have children write their estimates then have them make a train of snap cubes the same length as the toothbrush and count how many cubes are in it. Have them write 8.

5. Ask: *Did it take more paper clips or snap cubes to equal the length of the toothbrush?* It took more cubes. Help children realize it took more cubes because the cubes are shorter.

6. Have children estimate and measure the length of the pencil in snap cubes.

Unit Size and Measuring (continued)

Estimate how long or high.
Then measure real objects.

6.

estimate: about _____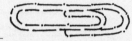

measure: about _____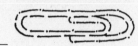

estimate: about _____

measure: about _____

7.

estimate: about _____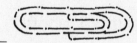

measure: about _____

estimate: about _____

measure: about _____

8.

estimate: about _____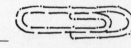

measure: about _____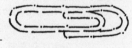

estimate: about _____

measure: about _____

Name _____

Inches and Feet

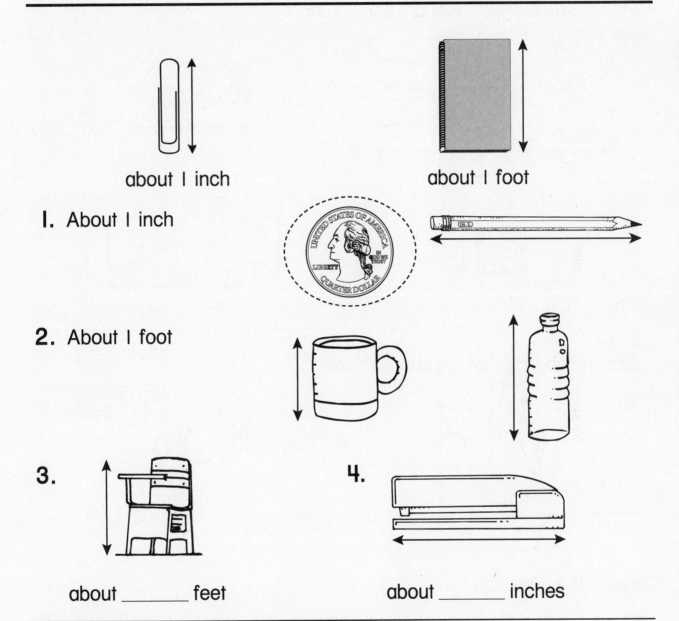

about 1 inch

about 1 foot

1. About 1 inch

2. About 1 foot

3.

about _____ feet

4.

about _____ inches

Materials: 10 paper clips and 1 notebook for each child, 12 inch ruler for demonstration

1. Show children one inch on the ruler. Tell them a paper clip is about one inch long. Show them one foot on the ruler and tell them a notebook is about 1 foot long.

2. Ask: *Which is about an inch, the length of a quarter or the length of a pencil?* Have children circle the quarter.

3. Ask: *Which is about a foot, the height of a mug or the height of a water bottle?* Have children circle the water bottle.

4. Say: *The plural for foot is feet. Would you use inches or feet to measure the height of your desk?* feet; Ask: *About how many feet high is your desk?* Have children write their estimates. Discuss reasonable estimates.

5. Ask: *Would you use inches or feet to measure the length of a stapler?* inches; Ask: *About how many inches long is the stapler?* Have children write their estimates. Discuss reasonable estimates.

Name _____

Inches and Feet (continued)

Circle the real objects that are about 1 inch.

5.

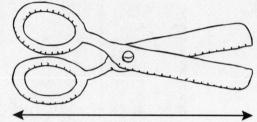

6.

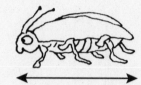

Circle the objects that are about 1 foot.

7.

Reasoning Estimate.

8.

about _____ inches

9.

about _____ feet

Name _____

Inches, Feet, and Yards

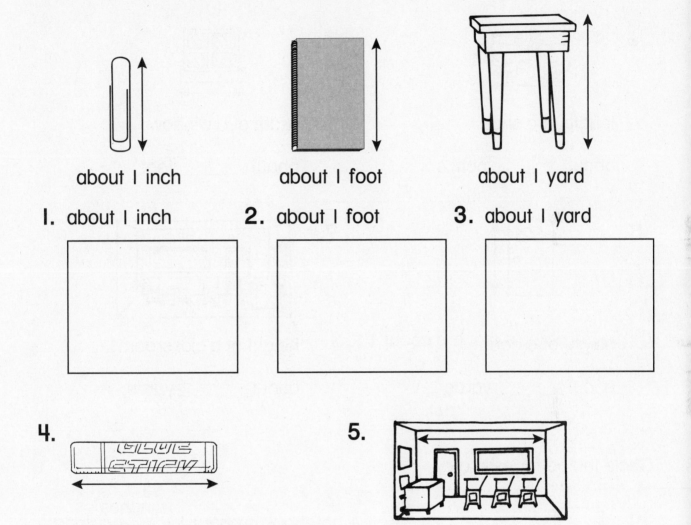

about I inch   about I foot   about I yard

I. about I inch

2. about I foot

3. about I yard

4.

about _____ inches

5.

about _____ yards

Materials: Yardstick and glue stick for demonstration

1. Show children one inch on the yardstick. Tell them a paper clip is about one inch long. Ask them to draw pictures in the first rectangle to show objects that are about one inch long, wide, or high.

2. Show children one foot on the yardstick. Tell them a notebook is about one foot long. Ask them to draw pictures in the second rectangle to show objects that are about one foot long, wide, or high.

3. Tell children the yardstick is one yard long and a desk is about one yard high. Ask them to draw pictures in the third rectangle to show objects that are about one yard long, wide, or high.

4. Show a glue stick. Ask: *Would you use inches, feet, or yards to measure the length of a glue stick?* inches *About how many inches long is a glue stick?* Have children write their estimates.

5. Ask: *Would you use inches, feet, or yards to measure the length of the classroom?* yards *About how many yards long is the classroom?* Have children write their estimates. Discuss the estimates.

Inches, Feet, and Yards (continued)

Estimate the width, height, or length of each real object.

6.

length of a shoe

about _____ inches

7.

width of a window

about _____ feet

8.

height of a door

about _____ yards

9.

height of a classroom

about _____ yards

Circle the better estimate.

10.

A notebook is about 12 (inches) yards long.

11.

A man is about 6 inches feet tall.

Name _____

Inches

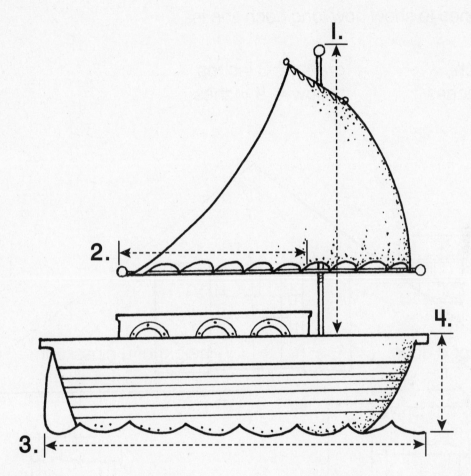

1. estimate _____ inches

   measure _____ inches

2. estimate _____ inches

   measure _____ inches

3. estimate _____ inches

   measure _____ inches

4. estimate _____ inches

   measure _____ inches

Materials: Inch rulers, 1 for each child

1. Show children an inch on a ruler. Ask them to find the line numbered 1 on the boat. Ask: *About how many inches long do you think the line is?* Have children write their estimates.

2. Draw a line on the board or overhead and demonstrate how to measure its length. Tell children to line up the zero on the ruler+ with one end of the line and read the number that is closest to the other end. Have children measure the line numbered one on the boat and write the measure.

3. Have children compare their measures to their estimates.

4. Have children estimate and then measure the other lines.

Name _____

Inches (continued)

Use a ruler. Measure each dotted line on the house.
Color the lines to show how long each line is.

red = 1 inch   green = 3 inches
blue = 2 inches   yellow = 4 inches

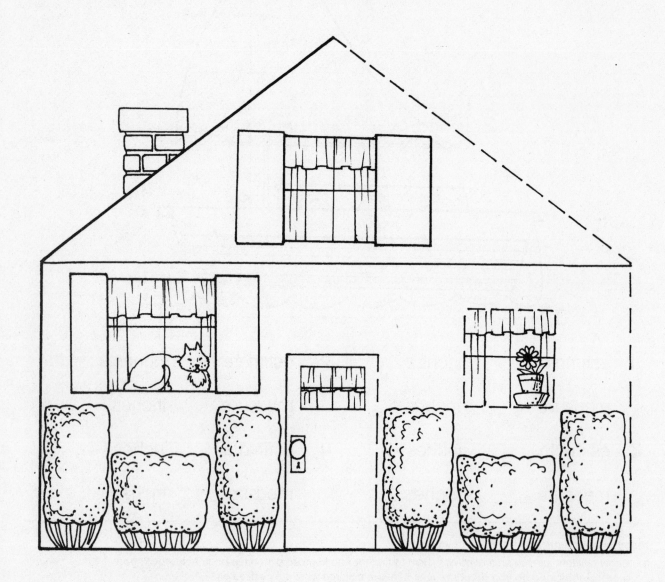

Name _____

Centimeters and Meters

1. about 1 centimeter

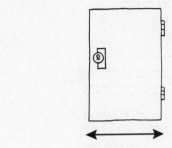

2. about 1 meter

about _____ centimeters

about _____ meters

Materials: meter stick and feather for demonstration

1. Show children one centimeter on the meter stick. Tell them a pencil is about one centimeter wide. Ask
    them to draw pictures in the first rectangle to show objects that are about one centimeter long or wide.

2. Tell children the meter stick is one meter long and a door is about one meter wide. Ask them to draw
    pictures in the second rectangle to show objects that are about one meter long or wide.

3. Show the feather. Ask: *Would you use centimeters or meters to measure the length of the feather?*
    centimeters *About how many centimeters long is the feather?* Have children write their estimates.
    Discuss the estimates.

4. Ask: *Would you use centimeters or meters to measure the length of the bulletin board?* meters
    About how many meters long is the bulletin board? Have children write their estimates. Discuss
    the estimates.

Centimeters and Meters (continued)

About how long or tall might the real object be?
Circle the better estimate.

5.

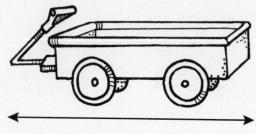

about 1 centimeter

about 1 meter

6.

about 30 centimeters

about 3 meters

7.

about 10 centimeters

about 1 meter

8.

about 1 centimeter

about 1 meter

9. Reasoning Would it take
more centimeters or meters
to measure your height?
Circle your answer.

centimeters

meters

Name _____

Centimeters

1. estimate: about _____ cm

   measure: about _____ cm

2. estimate: about _____ cm

   measure: about _____ cm

3. estimate: about _____ cm

   measure: about _____ cm

4. estimate: about _____ cm

   measure: about _____ cm

5. **Reasoning** 11 centimeters

Materials: centimeter rulers—1 for each child, glue stick, paperclip, stapler, and scissors for each group

1. Show children a centimeter on a ruler. Tell them cm is the abbreviation for centimeter. Ask: *About how many centimeters long do you think the glue stick is?* Have children write their estimates.

2. Draw a line on the board or overhead and demonstrate how to measure its length. Tell children to line up the zero on the ruler with one end of the line and read the number that is closest to the other end. Have children measure the length of the glue stick and write the measure.

3. Have children compare their measures to their estimates.

4. Have children estimate and then measure the other objects.

5. Have children circle the object which is the shortest.

6. Tell children to draw a line that is 11 centimeters long.

Centimeters (continued)

Estimate the length of each picture.
Then measure using a centimeter ruler.

6.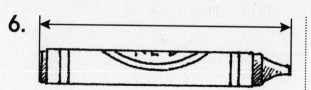

estimate: about _____ cm

measure: about _____ cm

7.

estimate: about _____ cm

measure: about _____ cm

8.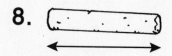

estimate: about _____ cm

measure: about _____ cm

9.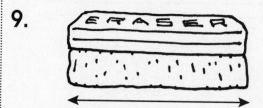

estimate: about _____ cm

measure: about _____ cm

10.

estimate: about _____ cm

measure: about _____ cm

11.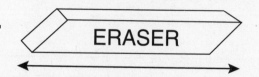

estimate: about _____ cm

measure: about _____ cm

Math Diagnosis and Intervention System
Intervention Lesson   **D28**

Exploring Capacity

1.

estimate: about _____ cups

measure: about _____ cups

2.

estimate: about _____ cups

measure: about _____ cups

3.

estimate: about _____ cups

measure: about _____ cups

Materials: For each pair or group, one small paper cup, rice or beans, and at least 3 different sized open containers like bowls, coffee cups, pans, and plastic or paper cups that hold more than the small paper cup

1. Have children choose one of the containers and draw a picture of it in the first box. Ask: *How many small paper cups of rice do you think it will take to fill the container you chose?* Have children write their estimates.

2. Have one child in each pair or group fill the small paper cup with rice and pour it into the chosen container. Have this child continue to do this as another child counts how many paper cups it takes to fill the container. When the container is full, have children write the measure. Then, have them compare the measure to their estimates.

3. Have children estimate and measure the other containers similarly, making sure every child has a turn at each task.

4. Have children circle the container that holds the most and put an X on the container that holds the least.

Exploring Capacity (continued)

Estimate how many cups each real object holds.

4.

       estimate: about _____ cups

5.

       estimate: about _____ cups

6.

       estimate: about _____ cups

7.

       estimate: about _____ cups

8. Reasoning Circle the best estimate.

     more than one cup   less than one cup

Name _____

Cups, Pints, and Quarts

 cup   **less than**   pint   **less than**    quart

I.

about I   about I   about I

2.

about I cup

about I pint

about I quart

Materials: One-cup measuring cup, pint milk carton, and quart milk carton, for demonstration

1. Show children the measuring cup and explain that it holds about one cup. Show the pint carton and explain that it holds one pint. Ask: *Which is more a cup or a pint?* pint; Show the quart carton and explain that it holds one quart. Ask: *Which is more a quart or a pint?* quart

2. Ask: *Does the pitcher hold more or less than a cup?* more *Does it hold more or less than a pint?* more *Does the pitcher hold more or less than a quart?* It holds about a quart. Have children circle the estimate for how much a pitcher hold.

3. Have children circle the best estimate for how much the glass holds.

Name _____

Cups, Pints, and Quarts (continued)

Circle the best estimate of each real container.

3.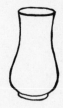

about I cup

about I quart

4.

about I cup

about I quart

5.

about I pint

about I quart

6.

about I cup

about I pint

7.

more than I cup

less than I cup

8.

more than I quart

less than I quart

9.

more than I quart

less than I quart

10.

more than I pint

less than I pint

11. Reasoning

A baby has a bottle of water.
About how much water does she have?

The baby has about a _____ of water.

Name _____

Liters

less than I liter

I liter

more than I liter

I.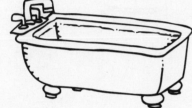

less than I liter

more than I liter

2.

less than I liter

more than I liter

3.

about 3 liters

about 30 liters

Materials: one liter bottle, gallon bottle, and juice carton for demonstration

1. Show the liter bottle and explain that it holds one liter. Show the juice box and ask: ***Does a juice box hold more or less than one liter?*** less; Show the gallon bottle and ask: ***Does a bottle like this hold more or less than one liter?*** more

2. Have children circle the best estimate for the bath tub and the small milk carton.

3. Show the liter bottle and ask: ***Suppose I filled up the liter bottle with water and poured it into an aquarium. Do you think I would need to do this about 3 times or about 30 times to fill the aquarium?*** about 30 times ***So the aquarium holds about 30 liters.*** Have children circle the estimate.

Liters (continued)

Circle the real container that holds **more than** 1 liter.

4.

5.

Circle the container that holds **less than** 1 liter.

6.

7.

8. **Reasoning** Circle the best estimate.

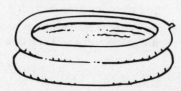

4 liters   1 liter   40 liters

Estimating and Measuring Weight

1.

4 cubes   10 cubes   20 cubes

2.

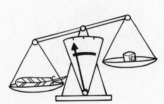

3.

Materials: Balance scale, snap cubes, and an object like a ball to measure, for demonstration

1. Introduce the balance scale. Explain that it is used to measure weight, or how heavy something is. Say: *When you put two objects on the balance scale, the heavier object makes its side of the scale go down. When the scale balances, the objects weigh the same.*

2. Have children look at the pictures of balance scales. Ask: *Which is heavier, the ball or 4 snap cubes?* the ball *Which is heavier, the ball or 10 snap cubes?* They weigh the same. *Which is heavier, the ball or 20 snap cubes?* 20 snap cubes

3. Put the object you have on one side of the balance scale. Have children guess how many snap cubes it would take to balance the scale. Start adding cubes and ask, which weighs more the object or 5 snap cubes, the object or 10 cubes, and so on. Find the weight of the object in snap cubes. If you do not have access to a balance scale, you can either skip this step or demonstrate with your hands and paper plates.

4. For items 2 and 3, have children look at each balance scale and circle the object which weighs more.

Estimating and Measuring Weight (continued)

Look at the balance scale.
Circle the object that weighs more.

4.

5.

6.

Name _____

Pounds

1.

> less than I pound

about I pound

more than I pound

2.

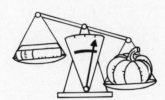

less than I pound

about I pound

more than I pound

3.

less than I pound

about I pound

more than I pound

4.

less than I pound

about I pound

more than I pound

Materials: A book which weighs about a pound, for demonstration

1. Tell children the book weighs about a pound. Ask: *Do you think a muffin weighs less than one pound, about one pound, or more than one pound?* Have children circle less than one pound.

2. Ask: *Do you think a pumpkin weighs less than one pound, about one pound, or more than one pound?* Have children circle more than one pound.

3. Ask: *Do you think a football weighs less than one pound, about one pound, or more than one pound?* Have children circle about one pound.

4. Have children estimate the weight of the bowling ball, similarly.

Name _____

Pounds (continued)

Circle the best estimate.

5.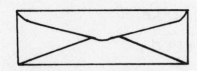

(less than I pound)

more than I pound

6.

less than I pound

more than I pound

7.

less than I pound

more than I pound

8.

less than I pound

more than I pound

9.

less than I pound

more than I pound

10.

less than I pound

more than I pound

II. Reasoning Circle the objects that weigh more than I pound.

**Math Diagnosis and
Intervention System**
Intervention Lesson   **D33**

Pounds and Ounces

I.   about 10 ounces

about 10 pounds

2.   about 5 ounces

about 5 pounds

3. 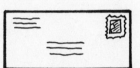   about 3 ounces

about 3 pounds

4. 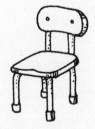   about 2 ounces

about 2 pounds

5.    about 1 ounce

about 1 pound

Materials: A book which weighs about a pound and a slice of bread, for demonstration

1. Tell children the book weighs about a pound and the slice of bread weighs about an ounce. Ask: *Do you think a baby weighs about the same as 10 slices of bread or as 10 books?* 10 books *So, does a baby weigh about 10 ounces or about 10 pounds?* Have children circle about 10 pounds.

2. Ask: *Do you think an apple weighs about 5 ounces or about 5 pounds?* Have children circle about 5 ounces.

3. Have children estimate the weights of the other objects, similarly.

Pounds and Ounces (continued)

Circle the best estimate.

6.

about 5 ounces

about 5 pounds

7.

about 15 ounces

about 15 pounds

8.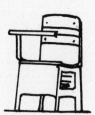

about 2 ounces

about 2 pounds

9.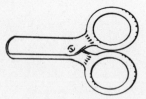

about 1 ounce

about 1 pound

10. Reasoning Circle the best estimate.

about 1 ounce

about 1 pound

about 10 pounds

Grams and Kilograms

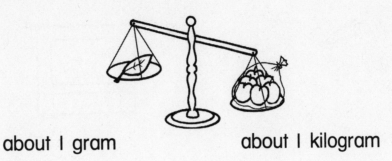

about I gram   about I kilogram

1.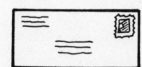

kilograms

2.  grams

kilograms

3. grams

kilograms

4.  grams

kilograms

5.  grams

kilograms

6.  grams

kilograms

Materials: A leaf and a bag of apples with a mass of about a kilogram, for demonstration

1. Show the leaf and tell children it measures about a gram. Show the bag of apples and tell children it measures about a kilogram.
2. Ask: *Would you use grams or kilograms to measure a hockey puck?* grams; Have children circle grams.
3. Ask: *Would you use grams or kilograms to measure a lamp?* kilograms; Have children circle kilograms.
4. Have children estimate the other objects, similarly.

Grams and Kilograms (continued)

Circle the best estimate.

7.

(grams)

kilograms

8.

grams

kilograms

9.

grams

kilograms

10.

grams

kilograms

11.

grams

kilograms

12.

grams

kilograms

13. **Reasoning** Is it more or less than 1 kilogram?
Circle the estimate.

Less than 1 kilogram   more than 1 kilogram

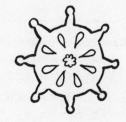

Name _____

Perimeter

I.

_16_ straws   _16_ inches

2.

3.

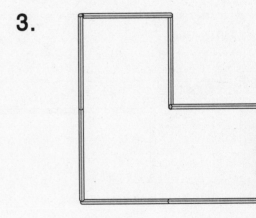

_____ straws   _____ straws

_____ inches   _____ inches

Materials: Pieces of drinking straws, cut into one-inch pieces, 16 for each child

1. Have children create the first shape with drinking straws. Ask: *How many straws did it take?* Have children write 16.

2. Say: *Each straw is one inch long, so the distance around the shape is 16 inches. The distance around a shape is its perimeter. What is the perimeter of the shape?* Have children write 16.

3. Have children create and find the perimeter of each of the other shapes similarly.

Perimeter (continued)

Find the perimeter of each shape. Each straw is one inch long.

4.

_____ inches

5.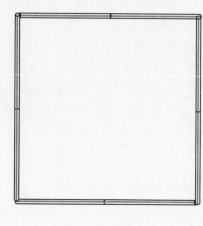

_____ inches

6.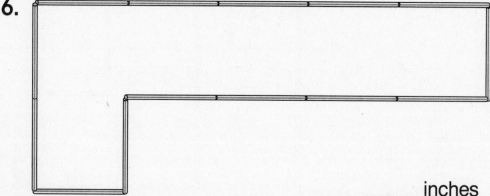

_____ inches

7. **Reasoning** Use 12 .
   Make a shape.
   Draw it.

Name _____

Exploring Area

1. __6__ square units

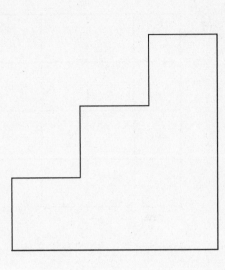

2. _____ square units

3. _____ square units

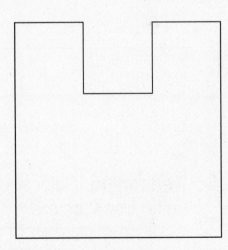

Materials: Pattern blocks squares or cut-out squares that are $\frac{3}{4}$–inch on a side, up to 8 for each child; crayons or markers

1. Ask: **How many squares does it take to cover the first shape?** Have children write 6.

2. Have children find the area of the other two shapes similarly.

3. Have children color the shape with the greatest area red. Ask: **How did you know that shape had the greatest area?** It has the greatest area because 8 is greater than 6 or 5.

4. Have children color the shape with the least area blue.

Exploring Area (continued)

Find the area of each shape.

4.

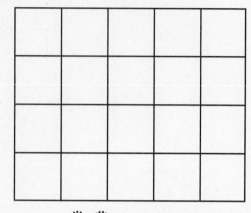

area: _20_ square units

5.

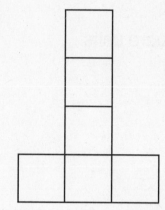

area: _____ square units

6.

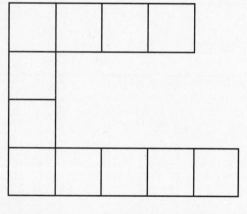

area: _____ square units

7.

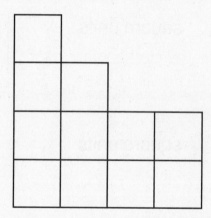

area: _____ square units

8. Reasoning Color two different shapes with an area of 10 square units. Use 2 colors.

© Pearson Education, Inc.

Name _____

Measuring Length to $\frac{1}{2}$ and $\frac{1}{4}$ Inch

Materials inch ruler for each student, crayons or markers.

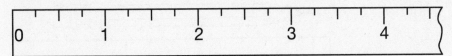

The distance between 0 and 1 on the ruler is one inch. So is the space between 1 and 2, 2 and 3, and so on.

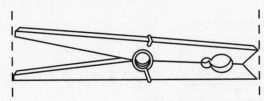

1. Line up the left edge of the clothespin with the 0 mark on the ruler. Is the clothespin's length closer to the 2 inch mark or the 3 inch mark?   _____

2. What is the clothespin's length to the nearest inch?   _____

3. How many spaces are between 0 and 1 on the ruler above?   _____

4. So each space is what part of an inch? _____

5. Color the marks in the ruler above that are $\frac{1}{4}$ inch and $\frac{3}{4}$ inch from zero red. Then color the rest of the $\frac{1}{4}$ inch marks red including $1\frac{1}{4}$, $1\frac{3}{4}$, $2\frac{1}{4}$, $2\frac{3}{4}$, and so on. Color the mark that is $\frac{2}{4}$ or $\frac{1}{2}$ inch from zero blue. Then color the rest of the $\frac{1}{2}$ inch marks blue, including $1\frac{1}{2}$, $2\frac{1}{2}$, and so on.

6. What is the length of the clothespin to the nearest $\frac{1}{2}$ inch? _____

Measure the length of the cricket to the nearest inch, $\frac{1}{2}$ inch and $\frac{1}{4}$ inch.

7. nearest inch   _____ inch

8. nearest $\frac{1}{2}$ inch _____ inches   9. nearest $\frac{1}{4}$ inch _____ inches

Name _____

Measuring Length to $\frac{1}{2}$ and $\frac{1}{4}$ Inch (continued)

Measure each object to the nearest inch, $\frac{1}{2}$ inch, and $\frac{1}{4}$ inch.

10. Nearest inch: _____ inches

11. Nearest $\frac{1}{2}$ inch: _____ inches

Nearest $\frac{1}{4}$ inch: _____ inches

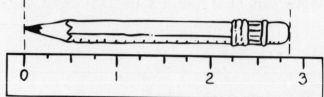

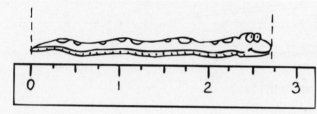

12. Nearest inch: _____ inches

13. Nearest $\frac{1}{2}$ inch: _____ inches

Nearest $\frac{1}{4}$ inch: _____ inches

14. Nearest inch: _____ inch

15. Nearest $\frac{1}{2}$ inch: _____ inches

Nearest $\frac{1}{4}$ inch: _____ inches

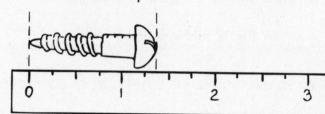

16. Reasoning Which gives the closest measurement, measuring
to the nearest inch, $\frac{1}{2}$ inch, or $\frac{1}{4}$ inch? Explain.

Name _____

Using Customary Units of Length

A small paperclip is about 1 *inch* long.

A football is about 1 *foot* long.

A baseball bat is about 1 *yard* long.

Most people can walk a *mile* in about 15 minutes.

What is the best unit to measure each?

1. The length of your pencil _____

2. The length of the Mississippi River _____

3. The height of a desk _____

4. The length of your school _____

Answer 5 to 7 and use the table to find how many inches are in 4 feet.

5. 1 foot = _____ inches

6. To find how many inches are in 4 feet, multiply 4 × 12 inches.

　　4 × 12 inches = _____ inches

7. How many inches are in 4 feet? _____

Customary Units of Length
1 foot (ft) = 12 inches
1 yard (yd) = 3 feet
1 yard = 36 inches
1 mile (mi) = 5,280 feet
1 mile = 1,760 yards

Answer 8 to 10 and use the table to find how many feet are in 5 yards, 2 feet.

8. 1 yard = _____ feet

9. How many feet are in 5 yards?　　5 × 3 feet = _____ feet

10. How many feet are in 3 yards, 2 feet?　　15 feet + 2 feet = _____ feet

Using Customary Units of Length (continued)

Which unit would you use to measure each item?
Write *inch*, *foot*, *yard*, or *mile*.

11. The length of a gerbil

_____

12. The length of a football field

_____

13. The height of a door

_____

14. The distance to the sun

_____

Circle the better estimate.

15. The distance you travel on
an airplane

560 yards   or   560 miles

16. The height of a full grown
adult giraffe

6 feet   or   6 yards

17. The length of a bar of soap

3 inches   or   7 inches

18. The length of your bed

7 feet   or   7 yards

Find each missing number.

19. 2 yards = _____ feet

20. 3 feet = _____ inches

21. 4 yards = _____ inches

22. 3 yards, 2 feet = _____ feet

23. 1 foot, 9 inches = _____ inches

24. 2 yards, 2 feet = _____ inches

25. Reasoning What unit would you use to measure the length
of an earthworm? Explain why your choice is the best unit.

Using Metric Units of Length

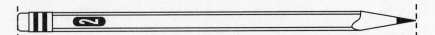

Materials centimeter ruler for each student

Your finger is about 1 centimeter wide.

1. Use the width of your finger to estimate the length of the pencil.

Estimate: _____ of my finger widths = about _____ centimeters

2. Line up the 0 mark on the ruler with the left edge of the pencil.

3. What is the length of the pencil
to the nearest centimeter?   _____

A dime is about 1 *millimeter* thick.

A new crayon is almost
1 *decimeter* long.

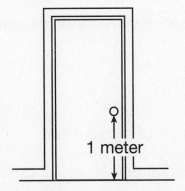

A door knob is about 1 *meter*
above the floor.

Most people can walk a
kilometer in about 10 minutes.

1 meter

What is the best unit to measure each?

4. the length of your finger   _____

5. the distance across your state   _____

6. the length of a lady bug   _____

Using Metric Units of Length (continued)

Answer 7 to 9 and use the table to find how many centimeters
are in 4 meters, 76 centimeters.

7. 1 meter = _____ centimeters

8. How many centimeters are
in 4 meters?

4×100 cm = _____ cm

9. How many centimeters are in
4 meters, 76 centimeters?

400 cm + 76 cm = _____ cm

Metric Units of Length		
1 centimeter (cm)	=	10 millimeters
1 decimeter (dm)	=	10 centimeters
1 meter (m)	=	100 centimeters
1 kilometer (km)	=	1,000 meters

Estimate the length of the spoon. Then measure to the
nearest centimeter.

10.

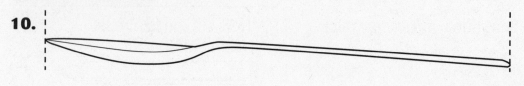

_____

What unit would you use to measure each item?
Write *millimeter, centimeter, decimeter, meter,* or *kilometer.*

11. An adult's height

_____

12. Distance traveled on vacation

_____

Choose the best estimate.

13. Length of a car

5 decimeters or 5 meters

14. Length of a calculator

12 centimeters or 12 decimeters

Find each missing number.

15. 3 meters 18 centimeters = _____ centimeters

16. 6 meters 3 centimeters = _____ centimeters

Name _____

Using Customary Units of Capacity

Materials 6 stations each equipped with the following: cup, pint,
quart, and gallon measuring containers labeled with
their units; one of 6 different sized containers to be
measured labeled A, B, C, D, E, and F; enough rice to
fill the container at least one and a half times; a piece
of paper taped into a funnel for containers with small
openings

The **capacity** of a container is the
amount the container can hold.

Go to each station. Find the row in
the table which matches the letter
on the container. Complete the table
by doing the following.

Customary Units of Capacity		
1 pint (pt)	=	2 cups (c)
1 quart (qt)	=	2 pints
1 gallon (gal)	=	4 quarts

- Decide what unit to use to measure the lettered container.

- Estimate the capacity of the container.

- Then measure the capacity of the container by filling the cup,
  pint, quart, or gallon container with rice and pouring it into
  the container until that container is full.

	Container	Best Unit	Estimate	Capacity
1.	A			
2.	B			
3.	C			
4.	D			
5.	E			
6.	F			

Using Customary Units of Capacity (continued)

What unit would you use to measure the capacity of each item?
Write *cup*, *pint*, *quart*, or *gallon*.

7. A pond

8. A watering can

9. A juice box

_____   _____   _____

10. A kitchen sink

11. A coffee mug

12. A pitcher of water

_____   _____   _____

13.

1 pt or 1 gal

14.

1 c or 1 qt

15.

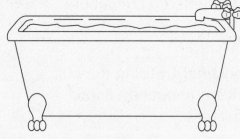

25 c or 25 gal

16.

2 c or 2 qt

17. Reasoning Martin bought a pint of grape juice. Franco
bought a gallon of orange juice. Seth bought a quart of
apple juice. List the type of juice in order from least to
greatest capacities.

_____

18. Reasoning Romona is making spaghetti. Explain why the
better estimate for the amount of water boiling in the pot is
2 quarts and not 2 cups.

Using Metric Units of Capacity

A water bottle holds about 1 liter.

A medicine dropper holds about
1 milliliter.

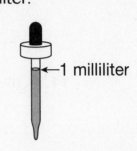

←1 milliliter

Garrison wants to find out how much
a small bottle of perfume holds.
Decide whether he should measure
the amount in liters or
milliliters by answering 1 and 2.

Metric Units of Capacity
1 liter (L)   =   1,000 milliliters (mL)

1. Would the perfume bottle hold more
   than a medicine dropper?   _____

2. Would the perfume bottle hold more
   than a water bottle?   _____

Since the perfume bottle holds less than 1 liter, it should be
measured in milliliters.

Decide whether 2 milliliters or 2 liters is a better estimate
for the amount of soup the bowl holds by answering 3 to 5.

3. Would 2 medicine droppers fill the bowl?   _____

4. Would 2 water bottles fill the bowl?   _____

5. Which is better estimate?   _____

6. **Reasoning** Explain why the better estimate for the
   amount of water a bucket holds is 8 liters and not
   8 milliliters.

Using Metric Units of Capacity (continued)

Choose a unit to measure the capacity of each item. Write *liters* or *milliliters*.

7. A can of soda

8. A swimming pool

9. A kitchen sink

_____   _____   _____

10. A birdbath

11. A measuring spoon

12. A soup bowl

_____   _____   _____

Circle the best estimate.

13.

4 L or 400 mL

14.

6 L or 650 mL

15.

7 L or 700 mL

16.

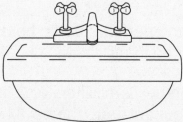

6 L or 60 mL

17.

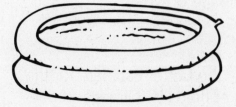

4 liters   1 liter   40 liters

Using Customary Units of Weight

The **weight** of an object is the measure of how heavy the object is.

A key weighs
about 1 ounce.

A football weighs
about 1 pound.

A bull weighs
about 1 ton.

Lucy wants to find out how much her
cat weighs. Decide whether she
should use ounces, pounds, or tons
by answering 1 to 3.

Customary Units of Weight
1 pound (lb) = 16 ounces (oz)
1 ton (T) = 2,000 pounds

1. Would the cat be
heavier than a key?   _____

2. Would the cat be heavier than a football?   _____

3. Would the cat be heavier than a bull?   _____

Since the cat would weigh more than a key, and more
than a football, but less than a bull, it should be measured
in pounds.

When measuring the weight of light objects, use ounces. When
measuring the weight of heavier objects, use pounds. When
measuring the weight of very heavy objects, like a bull, use tons.

Decide whether 4 pounds or 4 ounces is a better estimate for
the weight of a carrot by answering 4 to 6.

4. Would a carrot feel as heavy as 4 footballs? _____

5. Would a carrot feel as heavy as 4 keys?   _____

6. Which is a better estimate for the weight of a carrot,
4 ounces or 4 pounds?   _____

Using Customary Units of Weight (continued)

Choose a unit to measure the weight of each item. Write *ounces*, *pounds*, or *tons*.

7. Eyeglasses

_____

8. An adult whale

_____

9. A dog

_____

10. A tomato

_____

11. An eraser

_____

12. A school bus

_____

13. A ship

_____

14. A guitar

_____

15. A desk

_____

16. A mouse

_____

17. A motor scooter

_____

18. A feather

_____

Circle the best estimate for the weight of each item.

19. The space shuttle

45 lb   or   45 T

20. A bowling ball

10 oz   or   10 lb

21. A slice of bread

1 oz   or   1 lb

22. A turkey

15 oz   or   15 lb

23. A chicken

7 oz   or   7 lb

24. A hippopotamus

5 lb   or   5 T

25. Reasoning Explain why the better estimate for the weight of a pencil is 1 ounce and not 1 pound.

26. Reasoning If you had a bag of apples that weighed a pound and a bag of marshmallows that weighed a pound, which bag would have more items in it? Explain.

Name _____

Using Metric Units of Mass

The amount of matter in an object is its **mass**.

A cantaloupe has
a mass of about
1 kilogram.

A grape has
a mass of about
1 gram.

1 kilogram

1 gram

Chi wants to find the mass of a bag of
potatoes. Decide whether he should
use grams or kilograms by answering
1 and 2.

Metric Units of Mass
1 kilogram (kg) = 1,000 grams (g)

1. Would the bag be heavier than
   a grape?   _____

2. Would the bag be heavier than
   a cantaloupe?   _____

Since the bag of potatoes has a mass greater than a grape, and
greater than a cantaloupe, it should be measured in kilograms.

When measuring the mass of lighter objects, use grams. When
measuring the mass of heavier objects, use kilograms.

Decide whether 300 kilograms or 300 grams is a better
estimate for the mass of a bag of pretzels by answering 3 to 5.

3. Would a bag of pretzels feel as heavy as
   300 cantaloupes?   _____

4. Would a bag of pretzels feel as heavy as
   300 grapes?   _____

5. Which is the better estimate for the mass of
   a bag of pretzels, 300 kilograms or 300 grams? _____

Using Metric Units of Mass (continued)

Choose a unit to measure the mass of each item. Write *grams*
or *kilograms*.

6. car _____   **7.** pencil _____

8. calculator _____   **9.** dog _____

10. key _____   **11.** hairbrush _____

12. flowerpot _____   **13.** flower _____

Choose the better estimate.

14.

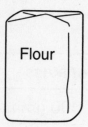

200 g   or   2 kg

15.

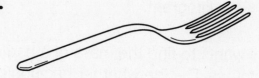

40 g   or   4 kg

16.

250 g   or   250 kg

17.

5 g   or   5 kg

18. Reasoning Why would you measure the mass of a goldfish
in grams and not kilograms?

19. Reasoning Explain why the better estimate for the mass of
a baby is 4 kilograms and not 4 grams.

Perimeter

Materials crayons or markers, centimeter ruler for each student.

Find the perimeter of the figure at the right by answering
1 to 3. **Perimeter** is the distance around a figure. Each
space between lines equals 1 unit.

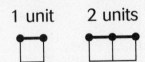

1 unit   2 units

1. Trace the figure with a crayon or marker. Count
the number of spaces as you trace.

2 How many spaces did you trace? _____

3. What is the perimeter of the figure? _____ units

scale: |—| = 1 unit

You can also find the perimeter by adding
the lengths of the sides.

Find the perimeter of the figure to the right
by answering 4 to 6.

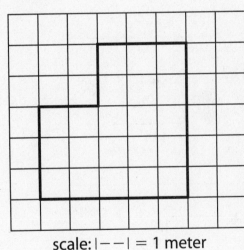

4. How many sides
does this figure have? _____

5. Trace over the sides as you count
and record the length of each side.

scale: |– –| = 1 meter

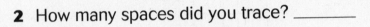

_____ + _____ + _____ + _____ + _____ + _____ = _____

6. What is the perimeter of the figure? _____ meters

Find the perimeter of the rectangle by answering 7 to 8.

Opposite sides of a rectangle have equal lengths.

7. Record the length of the sides. Find the sum.

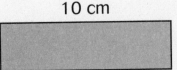

10 cm

3 cm

10 + 3 + _____ + _____ = _____

8. What is the perimeter of the rectangle? _____ cm

Perimeter (continued)

9. **Reasoning** Use a ruler to measure each side of the figure in inches. What is the perimeter of the figure?

_____

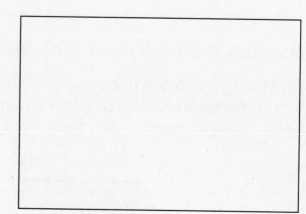

Find the perimeter of each figure.

10.

_____

11.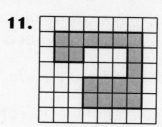

_____

12.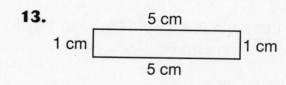

3 in.   5 in.

4 in.

_____

13.
5 cm

1 cm [   ] 1 cm

5 cm

_____

14.

9 cm

9 cm

_____

15.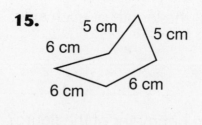

5 cm   5 cm
6 cm
6 cm   6 cm

_____

16. **Reasoning** If the length of one side of a square is 3 inches, what is the perimeter of the square? Explain your answer.

Name _____

Finding Area on a Grid

Materials crayons or markers

Area is the number of square units needed to cover the region inside a figure.

Find the area of the rectangle by answering 1 and 2.

1. Color each grid square inside the rectangle. Count as you color. How many grid squares did you color? _____

2. What is the area of the rectangle?

_____ square units

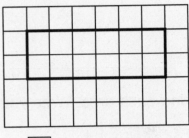

☐ = 1 square unit

Find the area of the polygon by answering 3 and 4.

3. Color each grid square inside the polygon. Count as you color. How many grid squares did you color? _____

4. What is the area of the polygon? _____ square feet

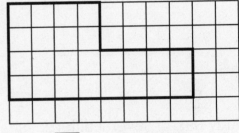

☐ = 1 square foot

Estimate the area of the triangle by answering 5 to 8.

5. Color the whole squares blue. How many squares did you color? _____

6. Combine partial square to make whole squares. Color the partial squares red. The partial squares make up about how many whole squares? _____

7. Add. 6 + 3 = _____

8. What is the estimated area of the triangle?

_____ square inches

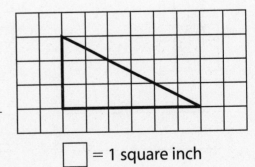

☐ = 1 square inch

Finding Area on a Grid (continued)

Find each area. Write your answer in square units.

9.

10.

11.

_____   _____   _____

_____   _____   _____

Find each area. Write your answer in square units.

12.

13.

14.

_____   _____   _____

_____   _____   _____

Judy baked several different shapes of crackers and wants
to know which is largest. Each cracker was placed on a grid.
Estimate the area of each cracker in Exercises 15 to 17.

15. Triangle

16. Hexagon

17. Quadrilateral

_____   _____   _____

_____   _____   _____

18. Which cracker in Exercises 15–17 has the greatest area?

Counting Cubes to Find Volume

Materials 28 unit cubes for each student

Answer 1 to 10 to learn how to find the volume of a prism.

1. Build the rectangular prism on the right.

2. How many cubes did you use?

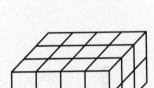

3. Build a second layer on the rectangular prism.

4. How many cubes did you
   use in the second layer?   _____

The **volume** of a figure is the number of
cubic units needed to fill it.

A **cubic unit** is a cube with edges that are 1 unit long.

5. Find the total volume of the rectangular prism.

    cubes in 1st layer   +   cubes in 2nd layer   =   total cubes

    _____   +   _____   =   _____

6. What is the total volume of the
   rectangular prism?   _____ cubic units

7. Build a third layer on the rectangular prism by
   putting a row of cubes on top of the back row.

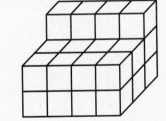

8. How many cubes did you
   use in the third layer?   _____

9. Find the total volume of the figure.

cubes in 1st layer	+	cubes in 2nd layer	+	cubes in 3rd layer	=	total cubes
_____	+	_____	+	_____	=	_____

10. What is the total volume of the figure?   _____ cubic units

Counting Cubes to Find Volume (continued)

Find the volume of each figure in cubic units.

11.

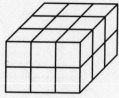

_____ cubic units

12.

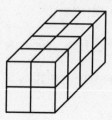

_____ cubic units

13.

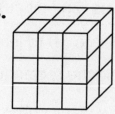

_____ cubic units

14.

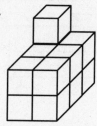

_____ cubic units

15.

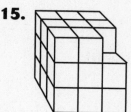

_____ cubic units

16.

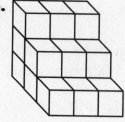

_____ cubic units

17. Reasoning Yao made a rectangular prism with 3 layers of cubes. He put 4 cubes in each layer. What is the volume of the rectangular prism?

_____ cubic units

18. Reasoning Box *A* consists of 8 cubic units. Three of Box *A* completely fills Box *B*. What is the volume of Box *B*?

_____

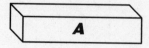

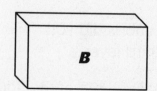

Name _____

Position and Location

Materials: Crayons or markers, objects for demonstration

1. Ask: **Are you inside or outside of school?** inside **What is outside in the picture?** Have children circle the kite and/or the cloud in red.

2. Hold an object **over** a table or desk. Ask if the object is **over** the table, **under** the table, or **on** the table. Repeat with **under** and **on** similarly. Have children use green to circle the objects in the picture that are **under** the table and orange to circle the objects that are **on** the table.

3. Point to a set of shelves. Ask which is the **top** shelf, the **middle** shelf, and the **bottom** shelf. Have children put an X on the **top** shelf in the picture with blue, on the **middle** shelf with yellow, and on the **bottom** shelf with purple.

4. Have children point to the picture of the tree on the back wall in the picture above. Ask: **What picture is above the tree?** Have children circle the Teddy bear picture with brown. Have them circle the picture **below** the tree with pink, **left** of the tree with yellow, and the picture **right** of the tree with purple.

Name _____

Position and Location (continued)

Use the picture of the table below.

1. Draw ☐ above the table.

2. Draw △ **under** the table.

3. Draw ⬭ **right** of the hat.

Use the stack of bowls below.

4. Color the **bottom** .

5. Color the **top** .

6. Color the **middle** 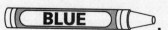.

Name _____

Shapes

Materials: Crayons or Markers

1. Have children color all the circles green.

2. Have children color all the squares orange, and all the triangles blue.

Math Diagnosis and Intervention System
Intervention Lesson   **D48**

Shapes (continued)

Color ▭ blue, △ green, ◯ yellow.

Solid Figures

1.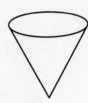

2.

3.

4.

Materials: Cylinder, cube, sphere, and cone geometric solids, crayons and markers

1. Show the cylinder. Tell children its name. Have them color the cylinder blue. Show and name the sphere and have children color the sphere green. Do the same for the cube and the cone. Have children color the cube red and the cone orange.

2. Ask children which shapes can be stacked. Demonstrate with the solids. Have them color the cube and the cylinder in item 2 orange.

3. Ask children which shapes can roll. Demonstrate with the solids. Have children color the cylinder, sphere, and cone in item 3 green.

4. Ask children which shapes slide. Demonstrate with the solids. Have children color the cylinder, cube, and cone in item 4 blue.

Solid Figures (continued)

Circle the object with the same shape.

5.

6.

Circle the shape that slides.

7. 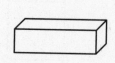   8.

Circle the shape that rolls.

9.    10.

Circle the shapes that stack.

11.   12.

Name _____

Flat Surfaces of Solid Figures

1.   ◯   ☐

2.   ◯   ☐

3.   ◯   ☐

4.   ◯   ☐

Materials: Cylinder, cube, sphere, and cone geometric solids

1. Show the cylinder and ask children its name. Ask: ***Does a cylinder have any flat surfaces?*** It has two.
   Ask: ***If you traced one of the flat surfaces, what shape would you get?*** Hold the cylinder against the board or overhead and trace around the bottom to make a circle. Have children ring the circle.

2. Repeat with the cube and the cone similarly.

3. Show the sphere. Ask: ***Does a sphere have any flat surfaces?*** no

Flat Surfaces of Solid Figures (continued)

Look at each shape.
Circle the object that has the flat surface.

5.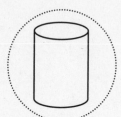

6.

7.

8.

9.

Name _____

Properties of Plane Shapes

1. Square

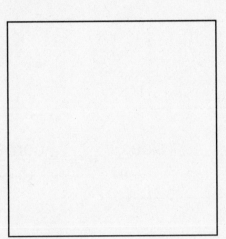

2. 3 corners

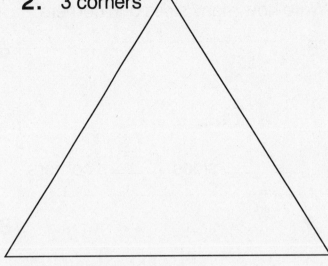

3. 0 corners

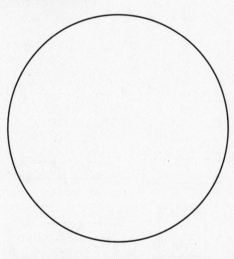

4. 6 sides

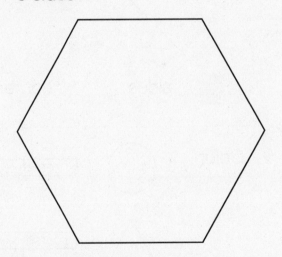

Materials: Attribute blocks, one triangle, one square, one rectangle, one circle, and one hexagon for each child or pair

1. Show a corner and a side of an attribute block. Have children touch one of each on a block.

2. Ask the children to choose the square and trace it in the first space on their paper. Ask: *How many sides does a square have?* Have children write 4 inside the square they drew. Ask: *How many corners does a square have?* Have children write 4 inside the square again.

3. Ask the children to choose the shape with 3 corners, trace it in the second space, and write the number of sides. Ask: *What is the name of the shape with 3 corners?* triangle

4. Ask the children to choose the shape with zero corners and trace it in the third space. Ask: *What is the name of the shape with 0 corners?* circle

5. **Reasoning** Ask the children to choose the shape with 6 sides, trace it in the last space, and write the number of corners.

Properties of Plane Shapes (continued)

Trace each side in a different color.
Draw an X on each corner.
Write how many sides and corners.

5.

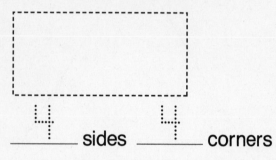

 _____ sides _____ corners

6.

_____ sides _____corners

7.

_____ sides _____corners

8.

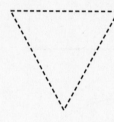

_____ sides _____corners

9. Color

  green

  orange

  red

  blue

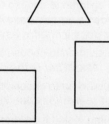

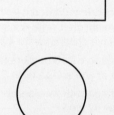

Making New Shapes from Shapes

1.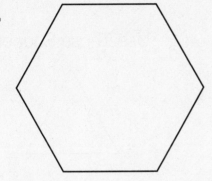

2.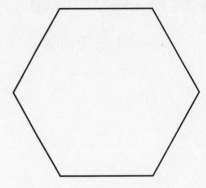

3.

4.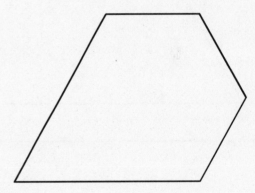

5.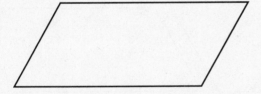

6.

**Materials: Pattern blocks, 2 hexagons, 2 trapezoids, 1 parallelogram, 3 rhombuses, and 7 triangles
for each child, pair, or group**

1. Show the rhombus pattern blocks. Have children use rhombus blocks to cover the first shape. Have
   them trace the blocks to show how they covered it.

2. Hold up a rhombus block. Say: ***You used these blocks to make a new shape.*** Hold up a trapezoid
   block. Ask: ***How can you use these blocks to make the same shape?*** Have children cover the
   second hexagon with trapezoid blocks and trace.

3. Have children use triangle blocks to make the shape in number 3 and then use a triangle and a
   rhombus to make the same shape in number 4.

4. Have children use a trapezoid and triangle block to make the shape in number 5 and triangle blocks to
   make the shape in number 6.

Making New Shapes from Shapes (continued)

Use pattern blocks to make each shape.
Draw the blocks you used.

Make This Shape	Use These Shapes

7.

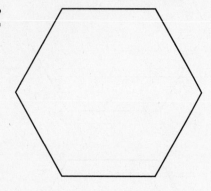

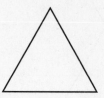

8.

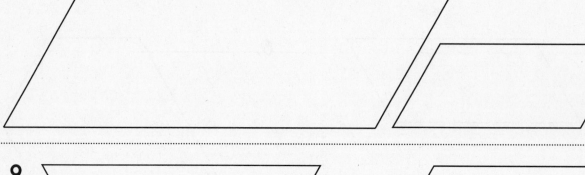

9.

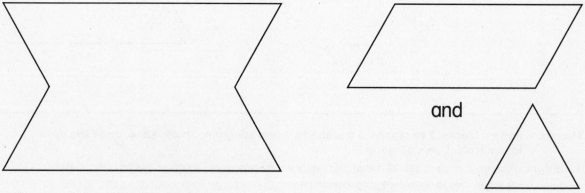

and

10. Create your own shape.
Show the blocks you used.

Name _____

Cutting Shapes Apart

1.

2.

3.

4.

5.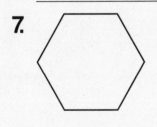

6.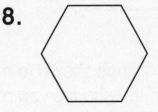

_____   _____

7.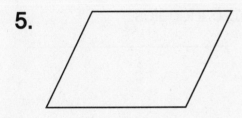

8.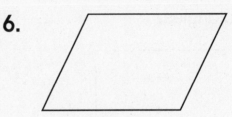

_____   _____

Materials: 3 pieces of spaghetti and a ruler or straightedge for each child, crayons or markers

1. Ask: *How could you cut the rectangle with one line to make 2 squares?* Have children use a piece of spaghetti to represent a line and try different ways to cut the rectangle. Have them use a ruler to draw a line that works.

2. Ask: *How could you cut the rectangle with one line to make two smaller rectangles that are not squares?* Have children find and draw a line using the spaghetti and ruler.

3. Have children cut the rectangle in number 3 with one line to make two triangles and the rectangle in number 4 with two lines to make 4 triangles.

4. Have children use two lines to cut the parallelogram into smaller shapes two different ways and list the shapes made.

5. Have children use 3 lines to cut the hexagon into smaller shapes two different ways and list the shapes made.

Cutting Shapes Apart (continued)

Draw lines to make new shapes.

9. Draw 1 line to make
2 triangles.

10. Draw 2 lines to
make 4 squares.

11. Draw 3 lines to make
6 rectangles.

12. Draw 3 lines to
make 6 triangles.

Draw the number of lines shown to make new shapes.
Write the names of the shapes you made.

13. 1 line

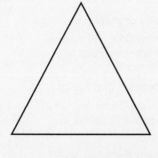

_____

14. 2 lines

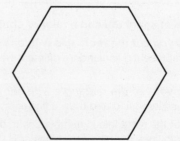

_____

Name _____

Same Size, Same Shape

1. 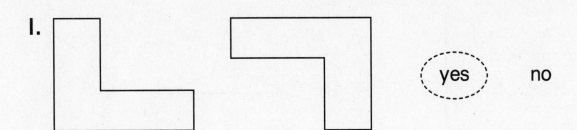   yes   no

2. 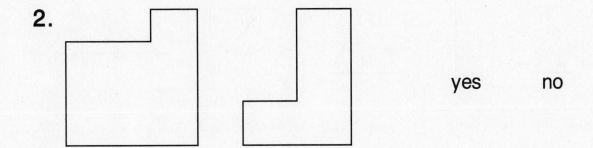   yes   no

3.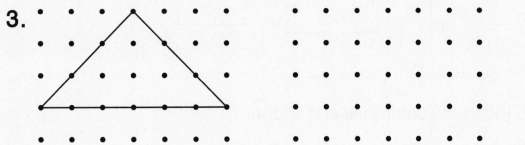

4.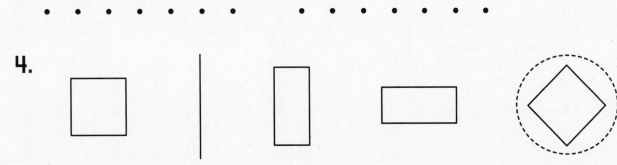

Materials: Tracing paper and scissors

1. Ask: ***Are the two figures the same size and shape?*** Have students circle yes. To check answer, have children trace the first shape, cut it out, and see if the tracing fits on the second shape.

2. Have children decide whether or not the second set of shapes match, similarly.

3. Have children draw a triangle that is the same size and shape as the triangle shown. Encourage children to count spaces between dots.

4. Have children circle the shape that is congruent to the first shape.

Name _____

Same Size, Same Shape (continued)

Circle the figure that has the same size and shape.

5. |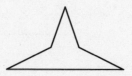

6. |

7. |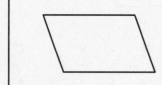

Draw a figure that is the same size and shape.

8.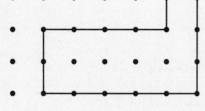

9.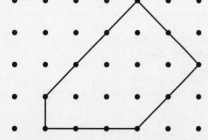

Ways to Move Shapes

Use this block.	Slide it.	Flip it.	Turn it.
1.			
2.			
3.			

Materials: Pattern blocks, 1 trapezoid, 1 rhombus, and 1 triangle for each child

1. Have children set a pattern block on the first shape in the table. Then have them slide it into the second column of the table and trace it.

2. Have children set the pattern block back on the first shape in the table. Then have them flip it into the third column of the table and trace it.

3. Have children set the pattern block back on the first shape in the table. Then have them turn it into the last column of the table and trace it.

4. Have children slide, flip, and turn the other pattern blocks similarly.

5. Have children look at the slide column. Ask: *How do the blocks look after a slide?* They look the same. *How do the blocks look after a flip?* They look like they would in a mirror. Ask: *How do the blocks look after a turn?* They look the same except turned another way.

Name _____

Ways to Move Shapes (continued)

Is it a slide, flip, or turn?

4.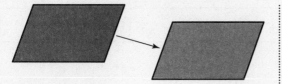

(slide)   flip   turn

5.

slide   flip   turn

6.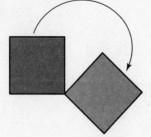

slide   flip   turn

7.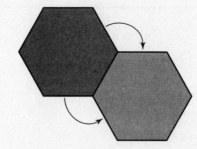

slide   flip   turn

8.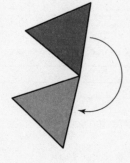

slide   flip   turn

9.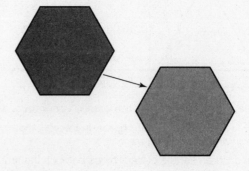

slide   flip   turn

Name _____

Symonetry

1.

2.

3.

4. Reasoning

Materials: Copy this page onto construction paper and either cut out the shapes for each child or provide scissors for children to cut out the shapes.

1. Have children cut the shapes out of the construction paper copy of the page, if not already done so.

2. Ask: *Can you fold the square to show matching parts?* Show children one way to fold the square. Show how the parts match. Have them draw a line on the first square to show matching parts.

3. Have children fold the other squares other ways and draw lines to show matching parts 3 other ways.

4. Have children fold the first triangle and draw a line to show matching parts.

5. Have children try to fold the second triangle. Ask: *Can you fold the triangle to show matching parts*? No

6. Have children draw a shape that has matching parts.

Symmetry (continued)

Circle each figure that has matching parts.

5.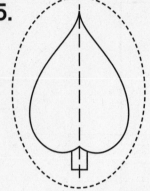

6.

7.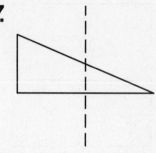

8.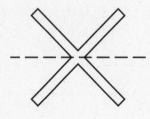

9.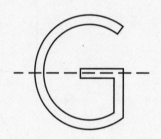

10.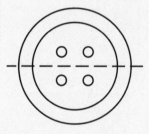

Draw a line to show matching parts.

11.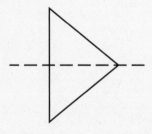

12.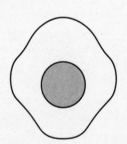

13.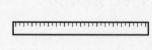

14. **Reasoning** Draw two lines
to show matching parts.

Flat Surfaces and Corners

Solid	Number of Flat Surfaces	Number of Corners
1.	6	8
2.		
3.		
4.		
5.		

Materials: Geometric solids for demonstration, crayons or markers

1. Show children a flat surface on the rectangular prism. Ask: *How many flat surfaces does the solid have?* Have children write 6 in the table.

2. Show a corner on the rectangular prism. Ask: *How many corners does the solid have?* Have children write 8 in the table. Tell children corners are called vertices and one corner is a vertex.

3. Show the cylinder. Ask: *How many flat surfaces does a cylinder have?* Have children write 2 in the table. Ask: *How many corners does it have?* Have children write 0 in the table.

4. Do the other solids similarly.

5. Have children solve some riddles. Say: *I have two flat surfaces and roll. Which solid am I?* Have children color the cylinder red.

6. Say: *I have 8 corners and cannot roll. Which solid am I?* Have children color the rectangular prism and the cube blue.

Name _____

Flat Surfaces and Corners (continued)

Color the figure that follows the rule.

6. I flat surface
no corners

7. 6 flat surfaces
does not roll

8. no flat surfaces
no corners

9. 2 flat surfaces
rolls

10. 6 flat surfaces
8 corners

11. Reasoning What rule tells how these
solid figures are alike?

    _____

Faces, Corners, and Edges

Solid	Number of Flat Surfaces	Number of Edges	Number of Vertices
1. rectangular prism			
2. cylinder			
3. cone			
4. pyramid			
5. sphere			
6. cube			

Materials: Geometric solids for demonstration

1. Show children a flat surface on the rectangular prism. Ask: *How many flat surfaces does the solid have?* Have children write 6 in the table. Tell children flat surfaces on objects that do not roll are faces. Ask: *Does a cylinder have faces?* no *Does a pyramid have faces?* yes

2. Show an edge on the rectangular prism. Ask: *How many edges does the prism have?* Have them write 12 in the table.

3. Show a corner on the rectangular prism. Ask: *How many corners does the solid have?* Have children write 8 in the table. Tell children corners are called vertices and one corner is a vertex.

4. Show the cylinder. Ask: *How many flat surfaces does a cylinder have?* Have children write 2 in the table. Ask: *How many edges does it have?* Have children write 0 in the table. Ask: *How many vertices does it have?* Have children write 0 in the table.

5. Do the other solids similarly.

Name _____

Faces, Corners, and Edges (continued)

Write the name of the solid. Find how many flat surfaces,
corners, and edges.

	Solid	Name	Flat Surfaces	Corners	Edges
7.		cylinder	2	0	0
8.					
9.					
10.					
11.					

Solid Figures

Materials power solids arranged in stations around the room

Find each solid to complete the tables below.

	Solid	Number of Faces	Number of Edges	Number of Vertices	Shapes of Faces
1.	Pyramid	5	8	5	1 square 4 triangles
2.	Rectangular Prism				
3.	Cube				

Objects that roll do not have faces, edges, or vertices.

	Solid	Number of Flat Surfaces	Shape of Flat Surfaces
4.	Cone	1	1 circle

Name _____

Solid Figures (continued)

	Solid	Number of Flat Surfaces	Shape of Flat Surfaces
5.	Cylinder		
6.	Sphere		

Name the solid figure that each object looks like.

7.

8.

9.

_____

_____

Use the solids in the table above to answer Exercises 10–12.

10. Which solid figure has 2 flat surfaces that are circles?

_____

11. Which of the 6 solid figures has 6 rectangular faces?

_____

12. Which 3 figures have no vertices?

_____

13. Reasoning How are the sphere and cone alike?

Name _____

Breaking Apart Solids

Materials power solids arranged in stations around the room,
index card one for each child

Find each shape. Discuss with your partner what the solid figure
would look like if it were cut horizontally. Draw a line to match
the cut solid with the correct description. Use your index card to
help visualize the cut. One description is used twice.

1.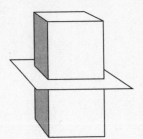

| two small rectangular prisms |

2.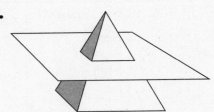

| two parts that each have 1 flat surface |

3.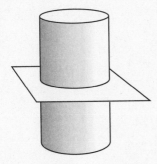

| a small cone and 1 other solid figure |

4.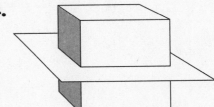

| two small cylinders |

5.

| a small pyramid and 1 other figure |

6.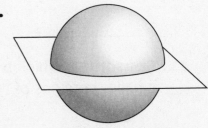

Breaking Apart Solids (continued)

Write the letters of the two smaller solids that make up the larger
solids in Exercises 7–10.

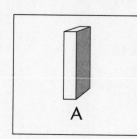
A

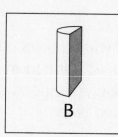
B

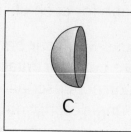
C

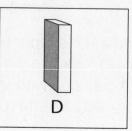
D

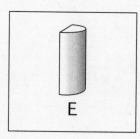
E

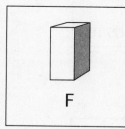
F

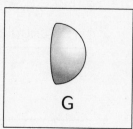
G

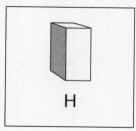
H

7.

_____

8.

_____

9.

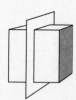

_____

10.

_____

11. Reasoning Which two solids, when cut in half, can form two
smaller versions of the solid itself?

Name _____

Lines and Line Segments

Materials crayons, markers, or colored pencils

A point is an exact place. It is shown by a very small dot.

1. Color in the circle to show a point.   ○

A *line* is an endless number of points going on forever in two
directions. There is no beginning and no end.

2. Color over the points to make a solid line.
Color in the two arrows to show the line
goes on forever in both directions.

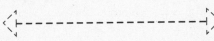

A *line segment* is a part of a line. It has a beginning and an end.

3. Color over the points to make a solid line segment.
Color in the points that are shown larger, to show
the line segment's beginning and end. These points
are called *endpoints*.

Box A	Box B
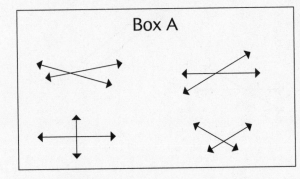	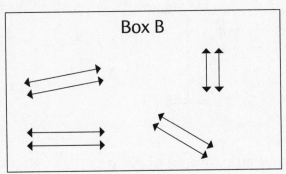

4. Reasoning How are the pairs of lines in Box A different
from those in Box B?

_____

Intersecting lines cross in a point. *Parallel lines* never cross.

5. What type of lines are shown in Box A?   _____

6. What type of lines are shown in Box B?   _____

Lines and Line Segments (continued)

7. Circle each figure with the color named below.

points—red   lines—blue   line segments—green

pairs of intersecting lines—orange   pairs of parallel lines—purple

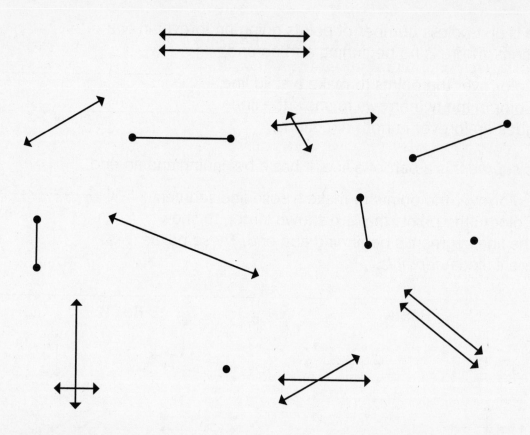

Draw an example of each.

8. parallel lines   **9.** line segment   **10.** line

11. Reasoning Draw an example of intersecting line segments.

Acute, Right, and Obtuse Angles

Materials 1 inch square piece of paper for each student, crayons or markers

A *ray* is part of a line. The endpoint is the beginning of the ray, and the arrow shows it goes on forever.

ray

An *angle* is made by two rays that have the same endpoint. That endpoint is called the *vertex*.

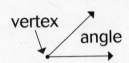
vertex   angle

1. Color each ray of the angle at the right, a different color.

Place a side of your square on one ray, and the corner on the vertex for each angle in 2 to 4.

2. Reasoning *Right angles* are shown below. What do you notice about the openings of right angles?

3. Reasoning *Obtuse angles* are shown below. What do you notice about the openings of obtuse angles?

Acute, Right, and Obtuse Angles (continued)

4. Reasoning *Acute angles* are shown below. What do you notice about the openings of acute angles?

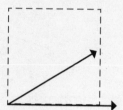

Write *ray, vertex, right angle, acute angle,* or *obtuse angle* to name each.

5.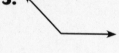

_____

6.

_____

7.

_____

8.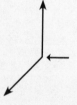

_____

9.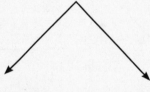

_____

10.

_____

What kind of angle do the hands of each clock show?

11.

_____

12.

_____

13.

_____

Name _____

Polygons

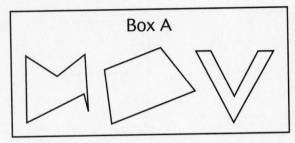

Box A

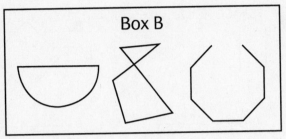

Box B

1. The figures in Box A are polygons. The figures in Box B are not.
How are the figures in Box A different from those in Box B?

To be a polygon:

- All sides must be made of straight line segments.
- Line segments must only intersect at a vertex.
- The figure must be closed.

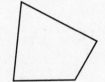

Polygons are named by the number of sides each has.
Complete the table.

	Shape	Number of Sides	Number of Vertices	Name
2.				Triangle
3.				Quadrilateral
4.				Pentagon
5.				Hexagon
6.				Octagon

Name _____

Polygons (continued)

Tell if each figure is a polygon. Write *yes* or *no*.

7.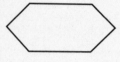

8.

9.

_____   _____   _____

Name each polygon. Then tell the number of sides and the number of vertices each polygon has.

10.

11.

_____   _____

12.

13.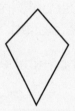

_____   _____

14.

15.

_____   _____

16. **Reasoning** What is the least number of sides a polygon can have?

_____

17. **Reasoning** A regular polygon is a polygon with all sides the same length. Circle the figure on the right that is a regular polygon.

 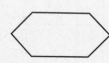

Name _____

Classifying Triangles Using Sides and Angles

Materials 2 yards of yarn, scissors, 6 sheets of construction
paper, markers for each student and glue

Create a book about triangles by following 1 to 7.

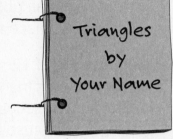

1. Put the pieces of construction paper together and
fold them in half to form a book. Punch two holes
in the side and use yarn to tie the book together.
Write "Triangles" and your name on the cover.

Each two-page spread will be about one type
of triangle. For each two page spread:

- Write the definition on the left page.
- Write the name of the triangle near
the top of the right page.
- Create a triangle with yarn pieces and
glue the yarn pieces under the name
of the triangle to illustrate the triangle.

2. Pages 1 and 2 should be about an **equilateral
triangle.** This triangle has 3 sides of equal length.
So, your 3 yarn pieces should be cut to the same
length.

3. Pages 3 and 4 should be about an **isosceles triangle.**
This triangles has at least two sides the same length.
Cut 2 pieces of yarn the same length and glue them
on the page at an angle. Cut and glue a third piece
to complete the triangle.

4. Pages 5 and 6 should be about a **scalene triangle.**
This triangle has no sides the same length. So your
3 yarn pieces can be cut to different lengths.

5. Pages 7 and 8 should be about a **right triangle.**
This triangle has exactly one right angle. Two of
your yarn pieces should be placed so that they
form a right angle. Cut and glue a third piece
to complete the triangle.

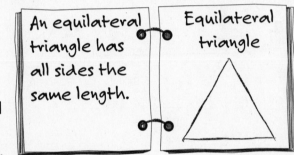

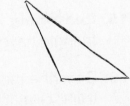

Classifying Triangles Using Sides and Angles (continued)

6. Pages 9 and 10 should be about an **obtuse triangle.** This triangle has exactly one obtuse angle. Two pieces of yarn should be placed so that it forms an obtuse angle. Cut and glue down a third yarn piece to complete the triangle.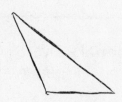

7. Pages 11 and 12 should be about an **acute triangle.** This triangle has three acute angles. Your 3 yarn pieces should be placed so that no right or obtuse angles are formed.

Tell if each triangle is equilateral, isosceles, or scalene.

8. 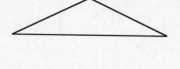   **9.** 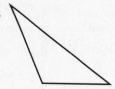   **10.**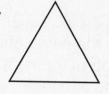

_____   _____   _____

Tell if each triangle is right, acute, or obtuse.

11. 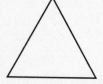   **12.** 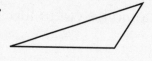   **13.**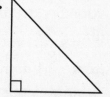

_____   _____   _____

14 How many acute angles does an acute triangle have? _____

15. Reasoning How many acute angles does a right triangle have? _____

16. Describe this triangle by its sides and by its angles. (Hint: Give it two names.)

_____

© Pearson Education, Inc.

Quadrilaterals

Materials Have quadrilateral power shapes available for
students who want to use them.

For 1 to 5 study each quadrilateral with your partner. Identify
the types of angles. Compare the lengths of the sides. Then
draw a line to match the quadrilateral with the best description.
Descriptions can be used only once.

1. Trapezoid

| Four right angles and all four sides the same length |

2. Parallelogram

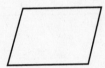

| All sides are the same length |

3. Rectangle

| Exactly one pair of parallel sides |

4. Square

| Two pairs of parallel sides |

5. Rhombus

| Four right angles and opposite sides the same length |

6. Reasoning What quadrilateral has four right angles
and opposite sides the same length, and can also
be called a rectangle?

_____

7. Reasoning What quadrilaterals have two pairs of
parallel sides, and can also be called parallelograms?

_____

Name _____

Quadrilaterals (continued)

For Exercises 8–13, circle squares red, rectangles blue, parallelograms green, rhombuses orange and trapezoids purple. Some quadrilaterals may be circled more than once.

8.   **9.** 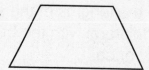   **10.**

11.    **12.**   **13.**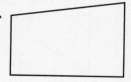

14. I have two pairs of parallel sides, and all of my sides are equal, but I have no right angles. What quadrilateral am I? _____

15. I have two pairs of parallel sides and 4 right angles, but all 4 of my sides are not equal. What quadrilateral am I? _____

16. Name all of the quadrilaterals in the picture at the right.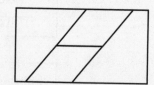

17. Reasoning Why is the quadrilateral on the right a parallelogram, but not a rectangle?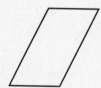

Congruent Figures and Motions

Materials construction paper, markers, and scissors

Follow 1–10.

1. Cut a scalene triangle out of construction paper.

2. Place your cut-out triangle on the bottom left side of another piece of contruction paper. Trace the triangle with a marker.

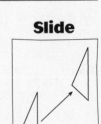

Slide

3. Slide your cut-out triangle to the upper right of the same paper and trace the triangle again.

4. Look at the two triangles that you just traced. Are the two triangles the same size and shape? _____

When a figure is moved up, down, left, or right, the motion is called a **slide**, or **translation**.

Figures that are the exact same size and shape are called **congruent** figures.

5. On a new sheet of paper, draw a straight dashed line as shown at the right. Place your cut-out triangle on the left side of the dashed line. Trace the triangle with a marker.

Flip

6. Pick up your triangle and flip it over the dashed line, like you were turning a page in a book. Trace the triangle again.

7. Look at the two triangles that you just traced. Are the two triangles congruent? _____

When a figure is picked up and flipped over, the motion is called a **flip**, or **reflection**.

Turn

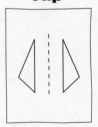

8. On a new sheet of paper, draw a point in the middle of the paper. Place a vertex of your cut-out triangle on the point. Trace the triangle with a marker.

9. Keep the vertex of your triangle on the point and move the triangle around the point like the hands on a clock. Trace the triangle again.

Congruent Figures and Motions (continued)

10. Look at the two triangles you just traced. Are the two
triangles congruent? _____

When a figure is turned around a point, the motion is a **turn**,
or **rotation**.

Write slide, flip, or turn for each diagram.

11.

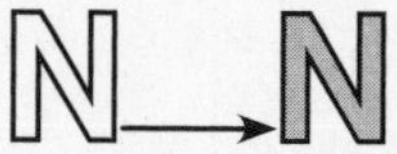

_____

12.

_____

13.

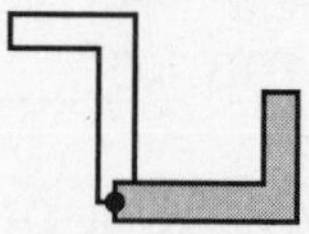

_____

14.

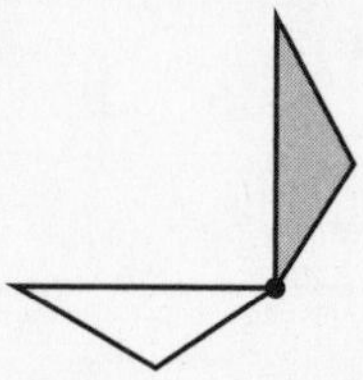

_____

15.

_____

16.

_____

For Exercises 17 and 18, use the figures to the right.

17. Are Figures 1 and 2 related
by a slide, a flip, or a turn?   _____

18. Are Figures 1 and 3 related
by a slide, a flip, or a turn?   _____

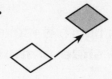

Figure 1

Figure 2

Figure 3

19. Reasoning Are the polygons at the right congruent?
If so, what motion could be used to show it?

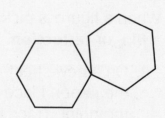

Line Symmetry

Materials one sheet of 3" x 3" paper, two sheets of 2" x 4"
paper, for each student

1. How many ways can you fold a rectangular sheet of paper
so that the two parts match exactly?

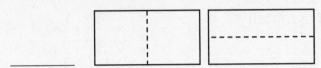

A **line of symmetry** is a line on which a figure can be folded so
the two parts match exactly.

2. Fold the square sheet of paper as many ways
as you can so the two sides match. One way
is shown at the right. How many lines of
symmetry does a square have?   _____

3. Cut a rectangular sheet of paper in half as
shown at the right. Cut out one of the
triangles formed.

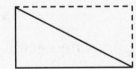

4. Fold the right triangle as many ways as you
can so two sides match. How many lines of
symmetry does the right triangle have?   _____

If a figure has at least one line of symmetry, it is **symmetric**.

5. Circle the figures that are symmetric.

To draw a symmetric figure, flip the given half over the line of symmetry.

Line Symmetry (continued)

Complete the figure below to make a symmetric figure by answering 6 to 8.

6. Find a vertex that is not on the line of symmetry. Count the number of spaces from the line of symmetry to the vertex.

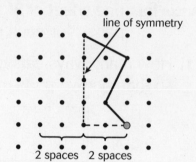

7. Count the same number of spaces on the other side of the line of symmetry and mark a point.

8. Use line segments to connect the new vertices. Do this until the figure is complete.

Decide whether or not each figure is symmetric. Write Yes or No

9.

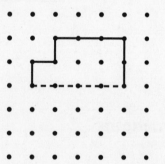

10.

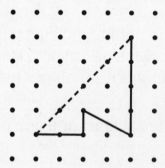

11.

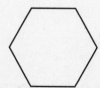

_____   _____   _____

Complete each figure so the dotted line segment is the line of symmetry.

12.

13.

Draw all lines of symmetry for each figure.

14.

15.

Name _____

Sorting and Classifying

Materials: Photocopy this page onto 3 or 4 sheets of construction paper, with each sheet a different color (use blue, red, and yellow) so there are enough shapes for each child to have one. Cut out the shapes and pin one to each child's shirt.

1. Ask the child with the large blue square and the one with the small red square, by name, to come to the front of the class. Ask: *Are the cut outs the same or different?* Lead a discussion to conclude that the shapes are the same shape but they are different colors and different sizes.

2. Ask one child with each different color of shape to go to a different corner of the room. Then ask the children who are still sitting to go to the corner where their shape belongs. If a child goes to a wrong corner, ask questions like the following: *What color is your shape? Where are all the other yellow shapes?*

3. Have all the children sit back down. Then repeat to sort by shape and then by size.

4. Ask, by name, the children with the small circles to come to the front of the class. Ask the children who are sitting to identify how the cut outs are sorted. Lead them to see that all the cut outs are small and circles.

5. Repeat with other combinations of attributes such as small red cut outs, or yellow rectangles.

Name _____

Sorting and Classifying (continued)

Color the one shape that is different.

1.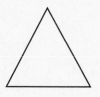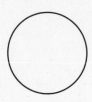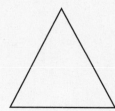

2.

3.

4. **Reasoning** Sort 2 ways.
   Circle one group to show 1 way.
   Color one group to show another way.

  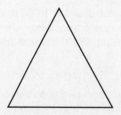

Name _____

Graphing

Materials: Crayons or markers, two-color counters, 4 for each child

1. Put children in groups of 4. Ask: *Would you rather play soccer or basketball?* Have children, within each group take turns answering the question. As each child answers, have all the children put a counter on the page. Have them put a red counter for soccer and a yellow counter for basketball.

2. Have children move the counter so each red one is in a square above the soccer ball and each yellow one is in a square above the basketball.

3. Say: *The graph you made is a picture of the data you collected.* Have children circle the column with more counters. Ask: *Which sport did more children in your group like to play?* Let each group tell the class the answer. Ask: *Which sport did fewer children in your group like to play?* Again, let each group tell the class the answer.

Name _____

Graphing (continued)

Color a square on the graph for each object.
Circle the object with more.

1.

 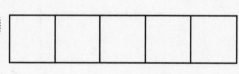

2.

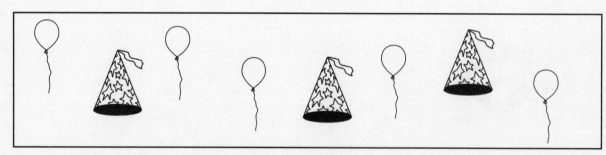

Reading Picture Graphs

Favorite Shapes

Each shape is 1 choice.

△ Triangle	△	△	△	△
○ Circle	○	○		

1. How many △ ? 4

2. How many ○ ? _____

3. △   ○

Favorite Movies

Science Fiction	🚀	⚇ ⚇ ⚇ ⚇ ⚇
Animal	🐕	⚇ ⚇ ⚇
Comedy	🐰	⚇ ⚇ ⚇ ⚇ ⚇ ⚇

4. How many?  _____

5. How many ? _____

6.

---

1. Ask children to look at the first graph. Tell them it is a picture graph of favorite shapes and each shape in the graph shows that 1 child chose that shape. Ask: **How many children chose the triangle?** Have children trace the 4.

2. Ask: **How many chose the circle?** Have children write 2.

3. Ask: **Which shape did more children choose?** Have children circle the triangle.

4. Ask children to look at the second graph. Tell them it is a picture graph of favorite types of movies: Science Fiction, Animal, and Comedy. Tell them each stick figure means 1 child chose that type of movie. Ask: **How many children chose Science Fiction?** Have children write 5.

5. Ask **How many chose Comedy?** Have children write 6.

6. Ask: **What type of movie did the most children choose?** Have children circle the cartoon character.

Name _____

Reading Picture Graphs (continued)

Use the graph to answer Exercises 7 to 12.

Favorite Frozen-Yogurt Flavor

Lemon 🍋	🍦🍦🍦🍦
Banana 🍌	🍦🍦🍦
Strawberry 🍓	🍦🍦🍦🍦🍦🍦🍦

7. How many like  best? _____

8. How many like best? _____

9. Which flavor did 4 children choose?

10. Which flavor is the favorite of the most?

11. Which flavor is the favorite of the least?

12. How many more chose than ? _____

Name _____

Reading Bar Graphs

Troy's Vacations

Beach   Camping   Parks

1.  _____

2.

3.

4.

© Pearson Education, Inc.

1. Tell children the graph is a bar graph which shows how many times Troy went to 3 different places for vacation. Ask: *How many times did Troy go to a park?* Have children find the top of the bar for parks. Then have them find the number that is even with the top of the bar and write 3.

2. Ask: *Where did Troy go 4 times?* Have children find the 4 and then find which bar is even with it. Have them circle the Beach picture in item 2.

3. For item 3, ask: *Where did Troy go the most?* Have children circle the Camping picture.

4. For item 4, ask: *Where did Troy go the least?* Have children circle the Parks picture.

Name _____

Reading Bar Graphs (continued)

Use the bar graph for Exercises 5 to 9.

Favorite Fruit

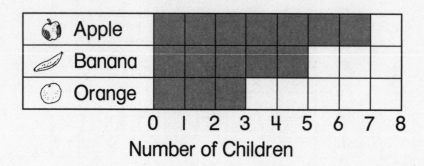

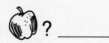

Number of Children

5. How many chose apples ? _____

6. Which did 5 choose?

7. Which was chosen by the most?

8. Which was chosen by the least?

9. How many more chose apple than orange ? _____

Name _____

Tallying Results

1.   Total

2.   **3.**

4. _____   **5.** _____

1. Say: **A tally chart can be used to organize information like the toys shown.** Show children how to make a tally mark. Have them cross out a drum and make a tally mark next to the drum in the chart. Have them cross out a Teddy bear and make a tally mark next to the Teddy bear in the chart. Show children how to cross 4 tallies with a fifth one. Explain that making groups of 5 makes it easier to count up the tallies. Have children continue crossing out toys and making tallies until all the toys have been counted.

2. Ask: **How many tallies do you have for the Teddy bear?** Have children write 8 in the total column of the chart. Repeat for the drum and top.

3. Ask: **Which toy has the most?** Have children circle the drum in item 2. **Which toy has the least?** Have children circle the top in item 3.

4. Ask: **How many more drums than Teddy bears are there?** Have children write 4 for item 4.

5. Ask: How many **Teddy bears and tops are there altogether?** Have children write 13 for item 5.

Name _____

Tallying Results (continued)

For Exercises 6 to 10, use the picture at the right.

6. Make tally marks to show how many of each there are. Then write each total.

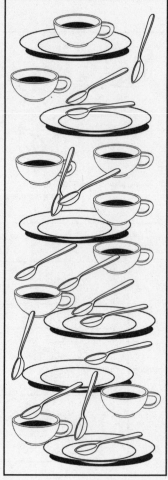

Total

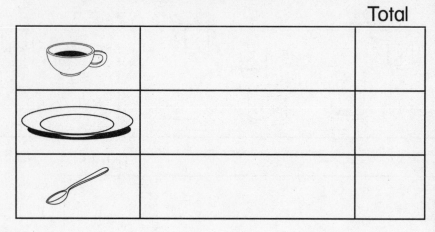

7. Which has the most?

8. Which has the least?

9. How many more spoons than cups? _____

10. How many cups and plates in all? _____

Real Graphs

Favorite Hats Tally Chart		
Cowboy 🤠	卌 I	
Ballet Tiara 👑	|||	
Baseball 🧢	卌	

I.

Favorite Hats Real Graph							
Cowboy 🤠							
Ballet Tiara 👑							
Baseball 🧢							

2.

3.

Materials: Snap cubes, 18 for each child

1. Ask children to look at the tally chart. Tell them it shows the favorite hats of some children. Ask: ***How many children chose the cowboy hat as their favorite?*** Have children count out 6 snap cubes. Have them put the snap cubes in the row of the graph with the cowboy hat, one cube in each space.

2. Repeat for the other two types of hats. Say: ***The real object graph makes it easy to compare the types of hats. Which hat was the favorite of the most children?*** Have children circle the cowboy hat in item 2.

3. Ask: ***Which hat was the favorite of the fewest children?*** Have children circle the tiara in item 3.

Name _____

Real Graphs (continued)

Use the tally chart to make a graph with cubes.

Animals Holly Saw at the Zoo Tally Chart		
Elephant	||||	4
Giraffe	|||	3
Monkey	|||||	5

4.

Animals Holly Saw at the Zoo Real Graph						
Elephant						
Giraffe						
Monkey						

5. What did Holly see the most?

6. What did Holly see the least?

Data and Picture Graphs

1.

Favorite Color Tally Chart		
Red		
Blue		
Green		

2.

Favorite Color Picture Graph						
Red						
Blue						
Green						

Each 웃 is 1 choice.

3. Most? _____

---

1. Form groups of 6 to 8 children. Ask: *Which color do you like the most, red, blue, or green?* Have children in each group take turns answering the question. As each child answers, have all the children in the group make a tally mark in the correct row of the tally chart.

2. Have children total the tallies and write the number in the chart.

3. Have children draw stick people in the first row of the picture graph. Tell them to draw one stick person for each tally mark next to red.

4. Have children do the same for blue and green.

5. Ask: *Which color was the favorite of the most children in your group?* Have children write the name of the color.

Data and Picture Graphs (continued)

4. Use tally chart to make a picture graph.

Our Pets Tally Chart		
Dog	ЖІ	
Cat	ІІІІ	
Fish	ІІ	

Our Pets Picture Graph						
Dog						
Cat						
Fish						

5. Which pet has the most? _____

6. Which pet has the least? _____

Name _____

Making Bar Graphs

Favorite Instruments Table		
Guitar		5
Banjo	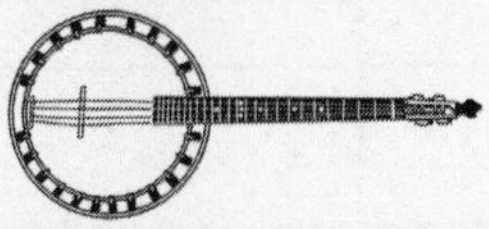	3
Piano		8
Drums	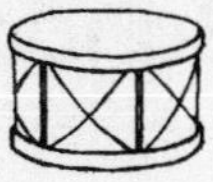	5

1.

Favorite Instruments Graph								
Guitar								
Banjo								
Piano								
Drums								

0   1   2   3   4   5   6   7   8

2. Most? _____

3. Least? _____

4. Same? _____ and _____

Materials: Crayons or markers

1. Tell children the table shows the favorite musical instruments chosen by several children. Ask: *How many children liked the guitar best?* Have children color the bar next to guitar in the graph, up to 5. Have children draw bars for each of the other instruments, similarly.

2. Ask: *Which instrument was the favorite of the most children?* Have children write piano.

3. Ask: *Which instrument was the favorite of the fewest children?* Have children write banjo.

4. Ask: *Which instruments got the same number of votes?* Have children write guitar and drums.

Making Bar Graphs (continued)

5. Use the table to make a bar graph.

How We Get to School Table	
Bus	7
Car	3
Walk	5
Bike	4

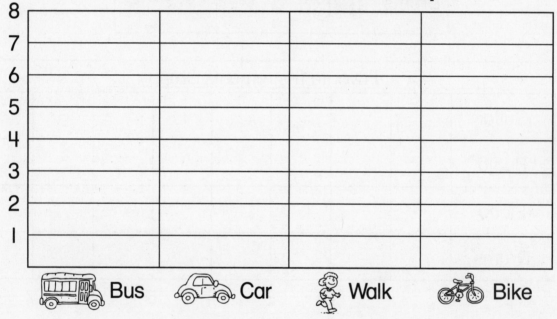

How We Get to School Graph

6. Tell the way most children get to school. _____

7. Tell the way the fewest children get to school. _____

Name _____

Locations on a Grid

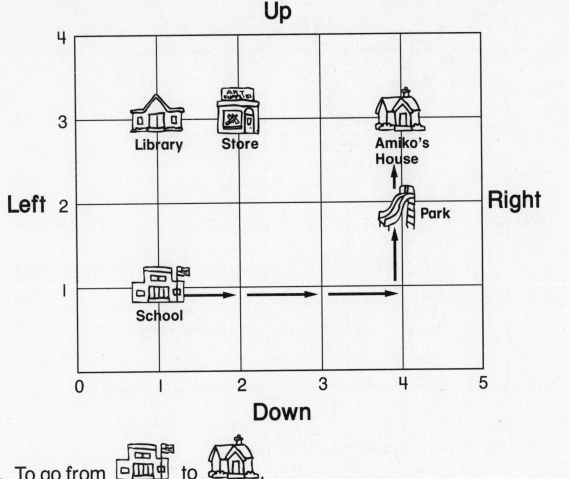

1. To go from 🏫 to 🏠,

go ___3___ blocks right and ___2___ blocks up.

2. To go from the 🏪 to the 🛝,

go _____ blocks right and _____ block down.

Materials: Snap cubes, 1 for each child. If possible, photocopy grid onto an overhead transparency for demonstration

1. Tell children the grid is a map of Amiko's town. Have children find the pictures of the school and Amiko's house on the map. Have the children put the snap cube on the school.

2. Say: *To travel on a grid, you travel left, right, up, or down by blocks. Each block is the space between grid lines. How can you get from school to Amiko's house?* Have children move the cube as shown by the arrows. Ask: *How many block did you move right?* Have children trace the 3. *How many blocks did you move up?* Have children trace the 2. Read the completed sentence in item 1.

3. Ask: *Is there another way to go from school to Amiko's house?* Have children use the snap cube to find another route. Say: *You can go up 2 blocks first and then right 3 blocks.*

4. Have children find a way to go from the store to the park and write their answers.

Name _____

Locations on a Grid (continued)

This is a map of Catie's town.

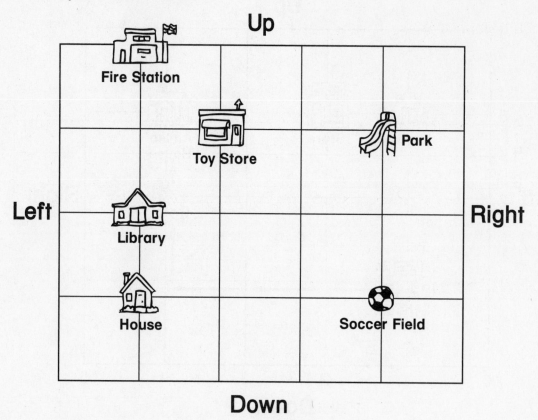

Read the map. Then complete each sentence.

3. To go from the 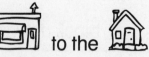 to the [slide],

go _3_ blocks right and _2_ blocks up.

4. To go from the [toy store] to the [house],

go _____ block left and _____ blocks down.

5. To go from the ⚽ to the [library],

go _____ blocks left and _____ block up.

Name _____

Range and Mode

Number of pets: 1, 4, 2, 1, 2, 2, 3, 1, 1, 4

1.

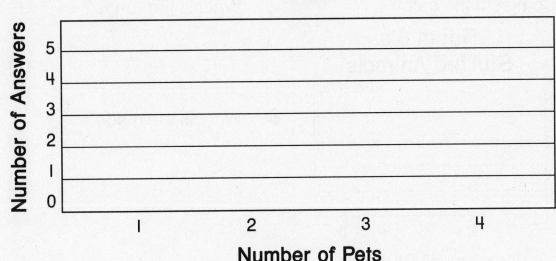

2. Greatest: _____

3. Least: _____

4. Range: _____

5. Mode: _____

Materials: Crayons or markers

1. Say: *A group of children told how many pets they have. The numbers listed at the top of the page are their answers. These numbers are called data. One child has 1 pet, one has 4, one has 2 and so on. How many children have one pet?* Have children color the bar above 1, up to the 4 mark. Have children finish the graph.

2. Ask: *What is the greatest number of pets the children have?* Have children write 4. *What is the least number of pets the children have?* Have children write 1. *The range is the difference between the greatest and the least number in the data. Find the range by subtracting 4 minus 1. What is the range?* Have children write 3.

3. Say: *Look at the bar graph. How many pets did the most children have?* The most children had 1 pet. *The number which shows up the most in a set of data is the mode. What is the mode of the data?* Have children write 1.

Name _____

Range and Mode (continued)

Use the data to answer the questions.
How many stuffed animals do children have?
Room 8 said: 1, 2, 4, 2, 5, 1, 2, 4, 2, 3

6. Complete the graph.

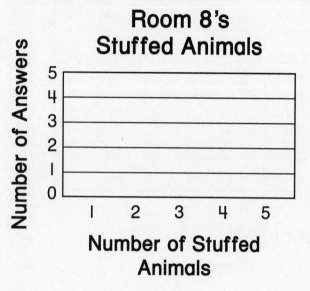

**Room 8's
Stuffed Animals**

7. What is the range?

_____ – _____ = _____

8. What is the mode?

_____

Room 9 said: 1, 3, 2, 3, 4, 1, 2, 2, 3, 3

9. Complete the graph.

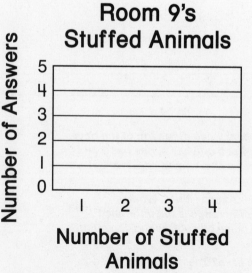

**Room 9's
Stuffed Animals**

10. What is the range?

_____ – _____ = _____

11. What is the mode?

_____

© Pearson Education, Inc.

Likely or Unlikely

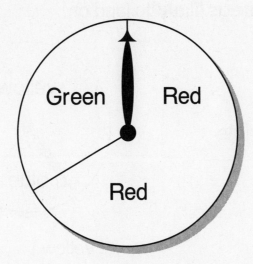

1.

Color	Tally
Red	
Green	

2. Most often? ___red___

3. Least often? _____

4. Likely? _____

5. Unlikely? _____

Materials: Crayons or markers, transparent spinners, 1 for each group

1. Have children color the red section of the picture of a spinner red and the green section green. Have one child in each group set the transparent spinner on the picture of a spinner so the centers match. Have that child spin the spinner 3 times. As the child spins, have the other children in the group put a tally next to the color the spinner lands on each time. Repeat until all the children in the group have had a chance to spin 3 times; make sure the total number of spins is at least 12.

2. Ask: *Which color did the spinner land on most often?* Have children trace the word red. *Which color did the spinner land on least often?* Have children write green.

3. *What color is the spinner likely to land on?* Have children write red. *What color is the spinner unlikely to land on?* Have children write green.

Likely or Unlikely (continued)

Color each spinner.
Circle the color each spinner is **likely** to land on.

6.

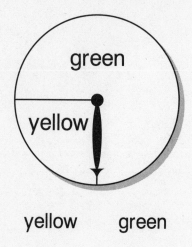

yellow   green

7.

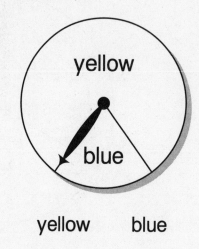

yellow   blue

Circle the color each spinner is **unlikely** to land on.

8.

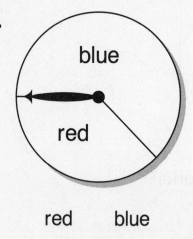

red   blue

9.

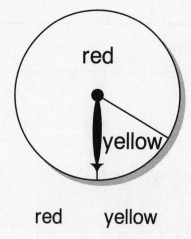

red   yellow

10. Reasoning Color the spinner
so red is likely and green is
unlikely.

Name _____

Certain or Impossible

1. certain

   impossible

2. certain

   impossible

3. is certain

4. is impossible

5. is impossible

6. is certain

Materials: 5 green snap cubes in an opaque bag for each group, crayons or markers

1. Tell children to not look in the bag. Have children in each group take turns pulling a snap cube out of the bag, saying its color, and then putting it back. Have them pass the bag around until every child has had 2 or 3 turns.

2. Ask: *What color snap cube did you get each time?* Have children color the first snap cube green. *If you pull a cube out again, what color would you get?* green; Say: *Pour out the cubes from the bag. You are certain to get a green cube when you pull a cube from the bag.* Have children circle certain.

3. Have children color the second cube yellow. Ask: *Is it possible to get a yellow cube from the bag?* no; Say: *It is impossible to get a yellow cube from the bag.* Have children circle impossible.

4. Have children color the first snap cube in item 3 blue. Ask: *If you are certain to get blue from the bag, what color should the other snap cubes in the bag be?* Have children color the other 5 snap cubes in item 3 blue.

5. Have children color the first snap cube in item 4 yellow. Have them color the other 5 snap cubes to make it impossible to pick yellow.

6. Have children color the first snap cube in item 5 green. Have them color the other 5 snap cubes a different way to make it impossible to pick green.

7. Have children color the first snap cube in item 6 brown. Ask: *If you are certain to get brown from the bag, what color should the other snap cubes in the bag be?* Have children color the other 5 snap cubes in item 6 brown.

Name _____

Certain or Impossible (continued)

Color the balloons to make each sentence true.

7. You are certain to pick an orange balloon.

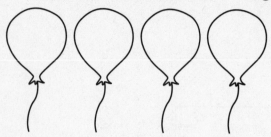

8. It is impossible to pick a yellow balloon.

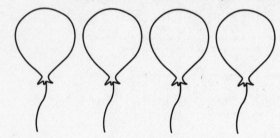

9. It is impossible to pick a red balloon.

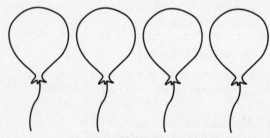

10. Reasoning You are certain to pick a yellow balloon
and it is impossible to pick a blue balloon.

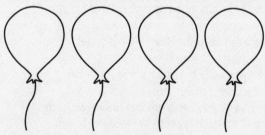

Name _____

Certain, Probable, Impossible

1.

Color	Tally
Yellow	
Green	
Blue	

2. Probable?　　　　　yellow　　　　green　　　　blue

3. Impossible?　　　　yellow　　　　green　　　　blue

4. Certain?　　　　　yellow or blue　　　　blue or green

5. Square

　　impossible　　　probable　　　certain

6. Triangle

　　impossible　　　probable　　　certain

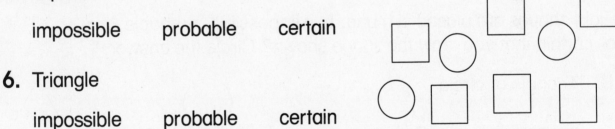

Materials: 15 snap cubes in an opaque bag for each group, with 12 blue and 3 yellow

1. Tell children to not look in the bag. Have children in each group take turns pulling a snap cube out of the bag, saying its color, and then putting it back. Have all the children in the group make a tally for each color. Have children pass the bag around until there are 30 tallies in the chart.

2. Ask: *What color snap cube did you get most often?* blue *If you pull out another cube what color would you probably get?* blue; Say: *So blue is probable.* Have children circle blue.

3. Ask: *Did you get any green cubes?* no; Have children look at the contents of the bag. *If you keep drawing out cubes, would you ever get any green cubes?* no; Say: *It is impossible to get a green cube.* Have children circle green.

4. Ask: *What colors will you get every time?* You will always get either blue or yellow. Say: *It is certain you will get either blue or yellow.* Have children circle yellow or blue.

5. Say: *Suppose the shapes shown are put in a bag and you pulled one out without looking. Is it impossible, probable, or certain that you draw a square?* Have children circle probable. *Is it impossible, probable, or certain that you draw a triangle?* Have children circle impossible.

Certain, Probable, Impossible (continued)

Seven shapes are placed in a bag. Is it impossible, probable,
or certain that you draw the shape shown? Circle the answer.

7. Circle

impossible   probable   certain

8. Rectangle or triangle

impossible   probable   certain

9. Rectangle

impossible   probable   certain

Eight shapes are placed in a bag. Is it impossible, probable,
or certain that you draw the shape shown? Circle the answer.

10. Triangle or circle

impossible   probable   certain

11. Circle

impossible   probable   certain

12. Square

impossible   probable   certain

Graphing Ordered Pairs

In the graph of the Animal Park, find what is located at (9, 8) by
doing the following.

In the ordered pair (9, 8),
the 9 is the *x*-coordinate.
It tells how far to move from
the origin along the *x*-axis.

The 7 is the *y*-coordinate. It tells
how far to move along the *y*-axis.

1. Start at the origin. Move
9 spaces right. Then, move
8 spaces up. What is at (9, 8)?

_____

2. What is located at (8, 4)?

_____

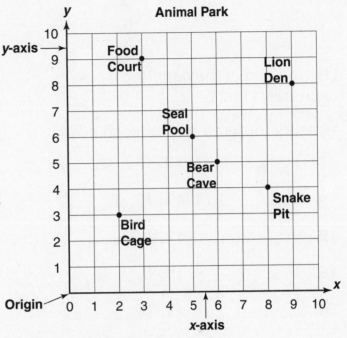

Find the coordinates of the Food Court, by doing the following.

3. Start at the origin. Move right along the *x*-axis until you are right
below the Food Court. How many units did you move right?   _____

4. So the *x*-coordinate, the first number in the ordered pair is _____.

5. Move up along the *y*-axis until you get to the Food Court.
How many units did you move up?   _____

6. So the *y*-coordinate, the second number in the ordered pair is _____.

7. Write the ordered pair that identifies the location of the
food court.   (_____, _____)

8. What is the *x*-coordinate of the Bird Cage? _____

9. What is the *y*-coordinate of the Bird Cage? _____

10. Write the ordered pair that identifies the location of the
Bird Cage.   (_____, _____)

Name _____

Graphing Ordered Pairs (continued)

11. Reasoning Use the graph of the Animal Park and compare the coordinates of the Seal Pool and the Bear Cave.

Use the grid at the right for Exercises 12–21.

Write the ordered pair for each point.

12. A _____   **13.** C _____

14. I _____   **15.** P _____

16. N _____   **17.** L _____

18. B _____   **19.** E _____

20. K _____   **21.** D _____

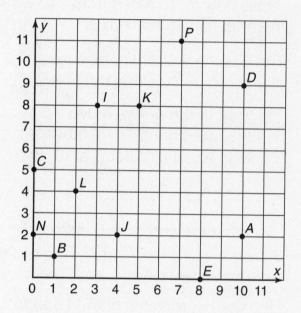

On grid paper, graph and label the point located by each ordered pair.

22. A (2, 2)   **23.** B (4, 2)

24. D (6, 6)   **25.** E (10, 0)

26. G (7, 8)   **27.** H (10, 4)

28. J (0, 1)   **29.** K (0, 10)

30. C (7, 1)   **31.** F (1, 3)

32. Reasoning You start at the origin and move 7 units right and zero units up and plot a point. What ordered pair identifies this point?

_____

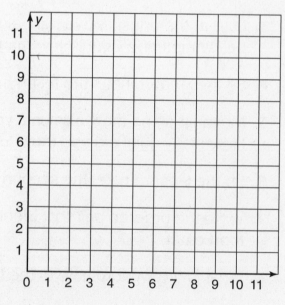

Recording Data from a Survey

Take a survey by asking, "What is your choice for a classroom
mascot: a falcon, a cougar, a stingray, or a bear?"

1. Write each student's answer in the box below.

Choice of Classroom Mascot

2. Make a tally mark for each choice given.
Remember, tallies are made in groups of
5 so that they are easier to count.

**Sample of
12 Tally Marks**

⊞⊞ ⊞⊞ ||

Choice of Classroom Mascot

Mascot	Tally	Total
Falcon		
Cougar		
Stingray		
Bear		

3. Count the tally marks. Record the total for each mascot choice.

4. How many students answered the survey? _____

5. Which mascot was chosen the most? _____

6. Which mascot was chosen the least? _____

Recording Data from a Survey (continued)

Favorite Season of the Year					
Summer	Fall	Summer	Winter	Spring	Fall
Winter	Summer	Spring	Fall	Fall	Spring
Summer	Winter	Winter	Winter	Summer	Winter

7. Complete the tally chart for the data above.

Favorite Season of the Year		
Time of Year	**Tally**	**Total**

8. What was the question for the survey?

_____

9. How many people answered the survey? _____

10. Which season was the favorite of the most people? _____

11. Which season was the least favorite of the people? _____

12. How many more people chose Summer over Spring? _____

13. Reasoning Write the seasons in order from least favorite to most favorite.

_____

14. Reasoning How many more people would have to have chosen Summer for it to be the most favorite season? _____

© Pearson Education, Inc.

Name _____

Reading and Making Pictographs

The members of Tom's class voted for their favorite pizza toppings. The results are shown in the tally chart at the right. Answer 1 to 7 to help you make and use a pictograph of the data.

Favorite Pizza Toppings		
Toppings	**Tally**	**Number**
Sausage	IIII	4
Vegetables	III	3
Pepperoni	IIII IIII	10

1. In the first row of the chart below write a title that best describes the pictograph. Then list the three toppings in the first column.

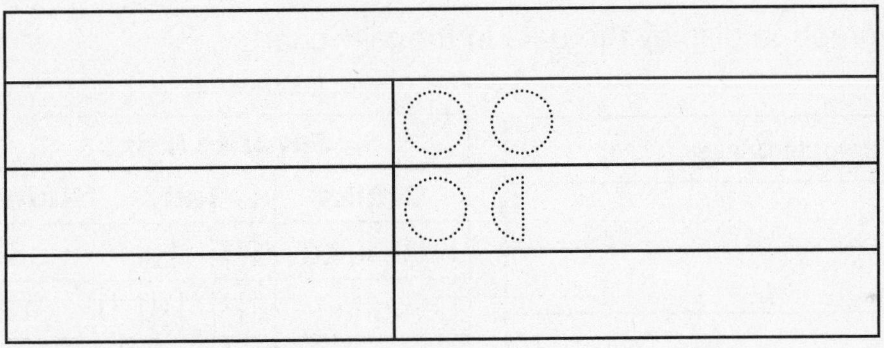

	◯ ◯
	◯ ◐

Each ◯ = 2 votes.   Each ◐ = _____ vote.

2. Complete the pictograph key.

3. Decide how many symbols are needed for each topping. Since sausage got 4 votes, draw 2 circles next to sausage. Since vegetables got 3 votes, draw 1 circle and 1 half-circle next to vegetables.

4. How many symbols are needed for pepperoni? _____

5. Draw 5 circles for pepperoni. Make sure you line up the symbols.

6. Which topping got the greatest number of votes? _____

7. Reasoning How can you tell which topping got the greatest number of votes by looking at the pictograph?

Name _____

Reading and Making Pictographs (continued)

For Exercises 8 to 11, use the pictograph shown at the right.

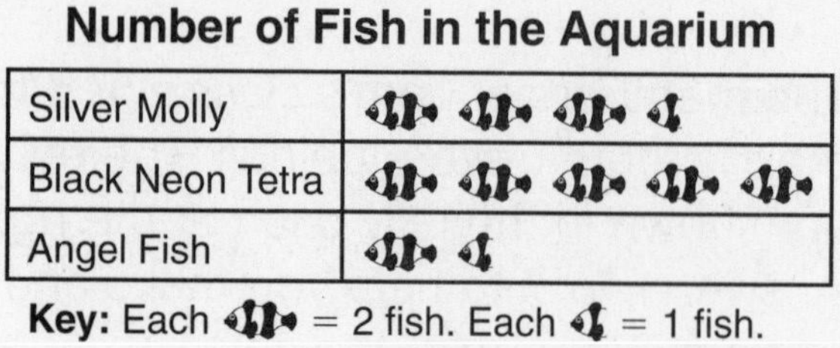

8. Which fish are there the most of in the aquarium?

_____

Number of Fish in the Aquarium

Silver Molly	⟨⟩ ⟨⟩ ⟨⟩ ⟨
Black Neon Tetra	⟨⟩ ⟨⟩ ⟨⟩ ⟨⟩ ⟨⟩
Angel Fish	⟨⟩ ⟨

Key: Each ⟨⟩ = 2 fish. Each ⟨ = 1 fish.

9. How many Silver Molly fish are in the aquarium? _____

10. How many more Black Neon Tetra fish are there than Angel Fish? _____

11. Make a pictograph to display the data in the tally chart.

Favorite Drinks	
Fruit Juice	
Lemonade	
Milk	

Key: Each 🥛 stands for _____ votes.

Favorite Drinks

Drinks	Tally	Number
Fruit Juice	⊞⊞ |||	8
Lemonade	⊞⊞ ⊞⊞ ||	12
Milk	||||	4

Use the pictograph you made in Exercise 11 to answer Exercises 12 to 15.

12. What does each 🥛 on the graph represent?

13. Which drink was chosen the least? _____

14. How many more people chose lemonade over milk? _____

15. Reasoning Do any kinds of drinks on the pictograph have the same number of votes? How do you know?

Reading and Making a Bar Graph

Materials colored pencils, markers, or crayons, grid paper.

Robert's class voted for their favorite country, not including the United States. The results are shown in the table.

Make and use a bar graph of the data by answering 1 to 6.

Our Favorite Countries	
Country	**Votes**
Canada	8
Great Britain	4
Japan	3
Mexico	11

1. Write a title above the graph. Label the axes: Country and Votes.

2. Complete the scale. Since the data go up to 11, make the scale by 2s.

3. Draw a bar for each country. Since Canada got 8 votes, color 4 squares above Canada, up to the 8 mark. For Japan, color one and a half squares because 3 is halfway between 2 and 4.

4. Which country got the least number of votes, that is, which has the shortest bar?

   _____

5. Which country got the greatest number of votes, that is, which has the longest bar?

   _____

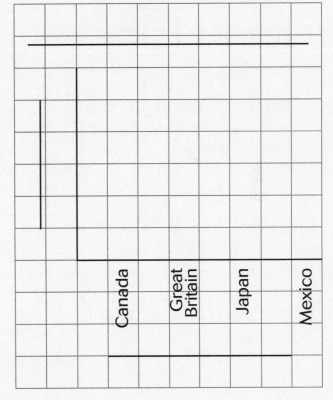

6. **Reasoning** Which bar is twice as long as the bar for Great Britain? What does that mean?

Reading and Making a Bar Graph (continued)

Use the grid on the right for Exercises 7 to 9.

7. Draw a graph of the data in the table.

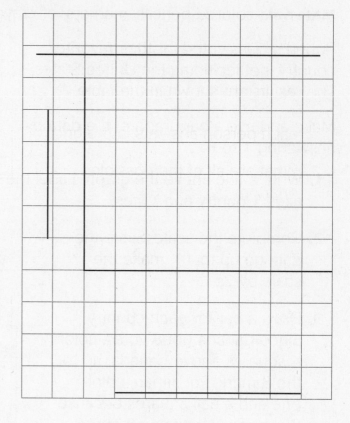

Cities We Want to See	
City	**Votes**
Anaheim	5
Orlando	12
Chicago	2
Washington	7

8. Which city got the most votes?

_____

9. Did twice as many students vote for Orlando as voted for Washington?

_____

Use the bar graph at the right to answer Exercises 10 to 12.

10. Which craft did most students say was their favorite?

_____

11. How many students chose boot making as their favorite craft demonstration? _____

12. How many more students chose wood carving than chose chair-caning as their favorite crafts?

_____

Favorite Crafts

Boot making
Chair-caning
Rug-hooking
Wood carving

Craft

Number of People

4   8   12   16

Making Line Plots

A year is sometimes divided into
quarters, as show at the right.

1st quarter: January to March
2nd quarter: April to June
3rd quarter: July to September
4th quarter: October to December

1. Take a survey by asking, "Which
   quarter of the year were you born?"
   Write the number of the quarter
   each person answers in the grid.

2. What are all of the possible
   quarters that can be said?

_____

Answer 3 to 7 to make and use a line
plot of the data.

3. Draw a line. Below the line,
   list in order, all the possible
   quarters that could be said.

Quarter of the Year You Were Born				

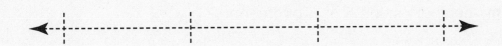

4. Write "Number of Birthdays by Quarter" below the line plot.

5. For each quarter that was said, mark an X above that quarter
   on the number line. If more than one X needs to be placed
   above a quarter, stack them in a single column.

6. Which quarter has the most number of birthdays?   _____

7. How many birthdays are after the 2nd quarter?   _____

Name _____

Making Line Plots (continued)

The nature club leader took a survey of the number of birdfeeders each member had made during camp. The results are shown in the table.

8. Make a line plot to show the data.

Birdfeeders Made During Camp

Member	Made	Member	Made
Ivan	4	Luther	5
Chloe	4	Marco	5
Stacey	3	Victoria	6
Victor	6	Chi	7
Tony	5	Wesley	5
Manny	6	Wendy	5

9. How many members made 4 birdfeeders? _____

10. How many members made 2 birdfeeders? _____

11. What was the most number of birdfeeders made by a member? _____

12. How many members made 5 or 6 birdfeeders? _____

13. How many members made less than 6 birdfeeders? _____

14. Did more members make more than 5 birdfeeders or less than 5 birdfeeders? _____

15. Reasoning By looking at the line plot, if one more person attended camp, do you think that person would probably make 4 birdfeeders or 5 birdfeeders? Explain.

How Likely?

Materials 1 yellow and 5 blue color tiles in a small paper bag,
for each child or pair

1. What are the possible color tiles
you could pull out of your bag?   _____ or _____

Each possible result is called an **outcome**. Pulling a tile from
your bag is called an **event**. The possible outcomes are getting
yellow or blue. Below are 4 ways to describe how likely an event is.

certain: It is sure to happen.	**likely**: It will probably happen.
impossible: It will never happen.	**unlikely**: It probably will not happen.

Draw a line to match the event with the likelihood for your bag.

2. Pulling a blue tile out of the bag.   Certain

3. Pulling a yellow tile out of the bag.   Impossible

4. Pulling a red tile out of the bag.   Likely

5. Pulling a colored tile out of the bag.   Unlikely

Below are 3 ways to compare the chances of two outcomes.

Outcomes with the same chance of happening are **equally likely**.
The outcome with a greater chance of happening is **more likely**.
The outcome with a lesser chance of happening is **less likely**.

6. Which color tile do you have more of?   _____
Getting blue is *more likely* than getting yellow.

7. What outcome is *less likely* than blue?   _____

8. Reasoning How many yellow tiles would you need
to make the outcome of getting a yellow tile
equally likely as getting a blue tile?   _____

Name _____

Math Diagnosis and
Intervention System
Intervention Lesson   **D86**

How Likely? (continued)

Use the spinner for Exercises 9 to 12.
Tell whether each event is likely, unlikely, certain,
or impossible when you spin the spinner.

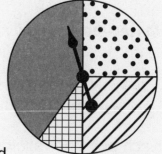

9. checked

_____

10. red   **11.** gray or dotted

_____   _____

12. gray, striped, dotted, or checked   _____

For Exercises 13 to 16, use the spinner above.

13. What outcome is more likely than dotted?   _____

14. What outcomes are equally likely?   _____

15. What outcome is less likely than striped?   _____

16. What outcomes are less likely than gray?

_____

17. Reasoning Draw a spinner for which the
chance of spinning A, B, or C is equally likely.

18. Reasoning Draw a spinner for which the chance
of spinning A is more likely than spinning B or C.

19. Reasoning How can you tell by looking at a
spinner that one outcome is less likely than
another outcome?

© Pearson Education, Inc.

Outcomes and Experiments

Materials transparent spinner, for each pair or group; red,
yellow, blue crayons

A **prediction** tells what may happen using
information you know.

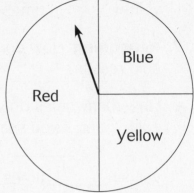

1. Color the spinner at the right.

If you spin the spinner 20 times, how many times
would you **predict** spinning each color? Answer
2 to 10 to make and test your predictions.

2. How many of the 4 equal parts of the spinner is each color?

_____ part yellow   _____ part blue   _____ parts red

So, if you spin the spinner 4 times you would predict that it
would land on yellow 1 time, blue 1 time, and red 2 times.

3. Complete the spinning
prediction table.

4. How many times do you
predict the spinner will land
on each color, if you spin
the spinner 20 times?

Yellow	1	2		4	
Blue	1		3		
Red	2	4			
Total Spins	4	8	12	16	20

yellow _____ times   blue _____ times   red _____ times

5. Place the transparent spinner
on the spinner above so the
centers match. Spin the
spinner 20 times. Make a tally
chart of your results.

Result	**Tally**	**Number**
Yellow		
Blue		
Red		

Name _____

Outcomes and Experiments (continued)

6. How many times did you spin each color in 20 spins?

   yellow _____ times   blue _____ times   red _____ times

7. Reasoning How do your predictions compare to your actual spin results?

8. How many times do you predict the spinner will land on each color, if you spin the spinner 40 times?

   yellow _____ times   blue _____ times   red _____ times

9. Spin the spinner 20 more times. Add the results to the tally chart above. How many times did you spin each color in 40 spins?

   yellow _____ times   blue _____ times   red _____ times

10. Reasoning Are your predictions closer to your actual spin results with 20 spins or with 40 spins? _____

11. Complete the table to predict the results of pulling a shape from the bag and returning it, each number of times.

Triangle	7	14	21	28	42	84
Circle	2		6		12	24
Square	1	2				12
Total Picks	10	20		40	60	

12. Complete the table to predict the results of spinning the spinner, each number of times.

Yellow	3	6				48
Blue	2					32
Total Spins	5	10	15	20	40	

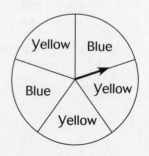

Line Plots and Probability

Materials 2 cubes, each numbered 1, 1, 2, 2, 3, 3 per pair

1. Toss the two number cubes. Find the sum of the two cubes. Record the sum in a box in the grid. Do this until all 30 boxes are filled.

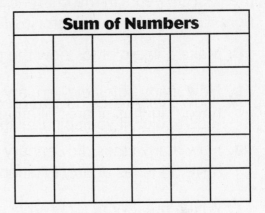

2. Find, then list all the possible outcomes for the sum of the two number cubes.

   $1 + 1 =$ _____ $1 + 2 =$ _____

   $1 + 3 =$ _____ $2 + 2 =$ _____

   $2 + 3 =$ _____ $3 + 3 =$ _____

   _____

Answer 3 to 7 to make and use a line plot of the results.

3. Draw a line. Below the line, list the possible outcomes in order from least to greatest.

4. Write a title below the line plot.

5. For each sum that was rolled, mark an X above that sum on the number line. If more than one X needs to be placed above a sum, stack them in a single column.

6. Which outcome has the most number of Xs? _____

7. **Reasoning** Predict the next sum most likely to be rolled and least likely to be rolled. Explain.

Line Plots and Probability (continued)

Larry recorded the total January
precipitation (to the nearest inch) for
the past 30 years in the chart at the
right. Use the data for Exercises 8 to 14.

January Inches of Precipitation					
4	6	3	4	5	4
7	7	5	3	4	5
3	4	5	5	6	7
3	1	4	2	6	5
5	5	5	1	2	1

8. Make a line plot to show the data.

9. How many times did January
have 4 inches of precipitation? _____

10. How many times did January
have 5 inches of precipitation? _____

11. Which number of inches occurred
4 times in the 30 years? _____

12. Which numbers of inches occurred the
same number of times?

_____

13. Reasoning Why was 0 not included
on your line plot?

14. Reasoning How many inches of
precipitation do you predict Larry's
area will have next January? Explain.

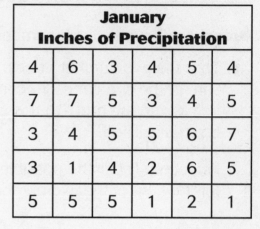

Making Bar Graphs to Show Outcomes

Materials 3 index cards (cut in half vertically), bag

1. Write each letter in the word "MUMMY" on an index card. Use the extra index card to make a tally chart for the possible outcomes: M, U, and Y.

2. Place the letters in a bag. Shake them and without looking pick a letter. Tally the letter. Replace the letter, shake, pick, and tally. Do this 20 times.

Answer 3 to 8 to make and use a bar graph of the results.

3. Write the title: Letters Picked from Bag above the graph and label the axes: Outcome and Number of Times.

4. Complete the scale. Make the scale by 2s.

5. Draw a bar for each letter. For every 2 tally marks for the letter M, color in one square above the letter M. After coloring a square for every 2 tallies, if you have a tally left over, color half of a square. Do this for U and Y.

6. Which two letters were picked about the same number of times?

   _____

7. Which bar is the longest? _____

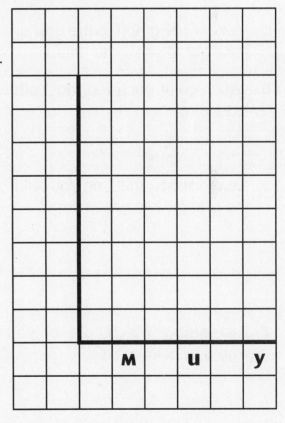

Since the bar above M is the longest, M is the outcome that occurred most often.

8. **Reasoning** Predict the next letter picked. Explain how you made your prediction.

Making Bar Graphs to Show Outcomes (continued)

Kendra spun a spinner 20 times. She recorded the number of
times each color was spun. Use the data for Exercises 9 to 13.

Spinner Results		
Outcome	**Tally**	**Number**
Purple	ⵊⵊⵊ ⵊⵊⵊ I	11
Green	IIII	4
Orange	IIII	4
Yellow	I	1

9. Make a bar graph in the grid on
the right to show the data.

10. Which color occurred most often?
least often?

_____

11. Reasoning What can you tell from
the orange and green bars?

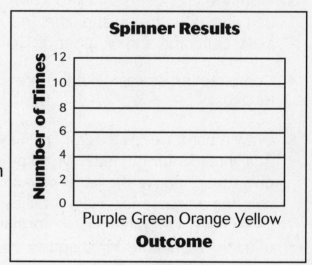

12. Reasoning Which color do you predict
would be spun next?

_____

13. Reasoning Draw what you think the spinner
looked like that Kendra used.

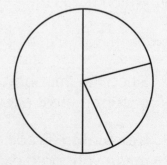